QS

EMULSION

UNDERCO

GLOSS

Victory in 'Site'!

Victory in 'Site'!

The 'Who-Dares-Wins' of Construction!

Sam Morley

Aedificamus Press

First published 1987 by
Aedificamus Press Ltd., The Ridgeway,
Northaw, Herts EN6 4BG

© 1987 Sam Morley

ISBN 0 9511701 0 4

Designed by Tina Dutton
Production in association with
Book Production Consultants, Cambridge.

Typeset by Goodfellow and Egan
Phototypesetting, Cambridge.

Printed in Great Britain by
Billings, Worcester.

List of Contents

List of Illustrations

Boatfuls of hopefuls!

Foreword

Construction isn't just digging holes and stacking a few thousand bricks on top of each other. A lot of water needs to pass under the bridge before that stage is ever reached. And on that stretch of water, 'boatfuls-of-hopefuls' – from architects to window-cleaners – may be seen pursuing a piece of the action.

The analogy conjures up a picture of a colourful water-side crowd scene. Something like those the French Impressionists used to do so well. Not being a Monet or a Renoir, I've tried painting it with words instead of oils.

An early draft was shown to a friendly architect, and then to an equally friendly builder. Their reactions were almost identical.

'A lot of it should be common knowledge both inside and outside the construction industry,' they said, 'but it isn't!'

'Get it published and circulated throughout the land,' they said, 'the world is waiting and just about ready for it.'

'Every client, consultant, contractor, and citizen,' they said, 'should be obliged by law to possess a copy!'

Well, they didn't quite say all that – but it's often the things people don't say that leave the deepest impressions.

With that, there follows an Impressionist word picture of the familiar Traditional scene!

When the 'picture' was first finished, I kept going over it, fussing around with cosmetic changes. It then occurred that the continuity might be better if some of the explanations were taken out of the text to form an appendix at the back of the book. There are four in all, and each makes a picture in its own right. Those stalwarts who struggle through to the end of the Postscript might well enjoy tackling the final 20 pages.

PART ONE

Who's Who in the Oldest Profession!

Prologue

The Construction Industry is the oldest profession on Earth. Don't just take my word for it – it's in the Book!

The opening 18 words of the Bible present the facts clearly for all to read:

'IN THE BEGINNING GOD created the heaven and the earth was without form, and void'.

That's exactly how they appear in my copy of the 350-year-old Authorised Version. In other words, it tells us that Earth was a virgin Construction Site, scheduled for a massive six-day development project.

The next 800 words describe those six days in rhetorical prose. No point in my reproducing all of it here, as anybody deciding to read this book is bound to have a copy of the Bible close at hand. But the salient passages are worth a mention because, paraphrased, their description of the first Six Days read like progress entries in a site diary. The entries would go something like this:

Date	Biblical passages	Site diary entry
Day One	'And the Spirit of God moved upon the face of the waters. And God said let there be light: and there was light . . . and God divided the light from the darkness . . .'	Site found to be flooded and completely under water. Temporary lighting installed to commence round-the-clock drainage programme.

Day Two   *1* . . . **A**nd God made the firmament, and divided the waters which were under the firmament from the waters which were above the firmament'.

Site drainage completed and project boundaries defined.

Day Three   *1* . . . **A**nd God said, Let the waters under the heaven be gathered together unto one place, and let the dry land appear: and it was so. . . . And God said, Let the earth bring forth grass, the herb yielding seed, and the fruit tree yielding fruit after his kind'.

Earth-moving and levelling completed. Landscaping completed. New ornamental lake formed to take drainage effluent. Plant delivered.

Day Four   *1* . . . **A**nd God made two great lights; the greater light to rule the day, and the lesser light to rule the night. He made the stars also. And God set them in the firmament of the heaven to give light upon the earth, and to rule over the day and over the night'.

Giant discharge luminaire delivered and installed. Also secondary system for emergency lighting to compensate for daily failure of main system.

Day Five / And God
. . . A created great
whales, and every living
creature that moveth,
which the waters brought
forth abundantly, after
their kind, and every
winged fowl after his
kind'.

Stocked
ornamental lake
with fish.
Bulk poultry
delivery to site
canteen.

Day Six / So God created
. . . S man in his
own image . . . and
said . . . replenish the
earth, and subdue it: and
have dominion over the
fish of the sea, and over
the fowl of the air, and
over the cattle, and over
every creeping thing that
creepeth upon the earth'.

General foreman
arrived to take
charge of sub-
contractors and
all site activity.

Now it doesn't actually say it in the Book, but it stands
to reason that, with all that work to be done in and around
Eden, Adam had to put up temporary buildings and site-
huts. Somewhere to keep tools and equipment, storage for
seeds and produce, shelter for himself and some of the
domestic animals when the weather turned a bit sour.
After all, there had to be some rain from time to time,
because we're told of a flowing river that kept Eden green
and fertile.

Even before Eden is mentioned we're told, 'there went
up a mist from the earth, and watered the whole face of
the ground'. Protection from the obvious prevailing damp
conditions must have been a top priority on site.

Not until everything had settled down nicely in the
Garden of Eden was it decided to send Adam a bit of extra

help, in the shape of Eve. And it was that naughty old shape of Eve that got the wrong profession the reputation of being the oldest!

Now we've got the record straight the up-dated story can be told. The same three words that introduced the Original Development Project can be used again as a curtain-raiser. This time to prepare the way for a traditional construction scene:

──2──

Genesis

IN THE BEGINNING . . . there must be a CLIENT. Like his Creator, Client is omnipotent, at least as far as the building project in question is concerned. He must only be written or thought of with a capital C.

Client can be a speculative Property Developer, a multinational Hotel Group, an Oil Conglomerate, a Hospital Board, a University, a Bank, a Government Department, the Church Commissioners – the list is long, and individual requirements as to shapes and interior layouts differ as widely as the respective interests. Other than pop-stars and Arabs, Client is rarely a person.

To earn the title, the controlling body of a would-be Client needs to decide to construct a new building. Or refurbish an old one. They've also got to be sure they can put their hands on sufficient funds to finance the job. It doesn't have to be their money. In fact it seldom is. It usually comes from taxpayers, ratepayers, investors, or shareholders. In other words – you and me. But once Client fancies an ego-trip, he likes to think he can take our blessing for granted.

For the purpose of this exercise we'll need to give our Client-figure a name. Insurance companies have long been good customers to the construction industry, so let's call Client, 'The Prummercial Assurance Group plc.' (P.A.G.) To the best of my knowledge there is nobody trading with that title. But if there is, then let me put it on record now that no inference is intended.

With its coffers bulging with paid-up premiums of half-a-million pension-and-security-minded investors, P.A.G. decides to change its corporate image by building a new

6

H.Q. in the City of London. Their closest rival, the Con-
federate Union Group, is shortly moving into its new
Head Offices a quarter-mile away: 16 floors of computerised administration, clad in black Italian marble. Compar-
ing the balance sheets and growth records of the two
companies, P.A.G. decides on a 20-storey job – in onyx!

Well, that's the concept. Turning it into a project needs
professional skills. First and foremost – an Architect. Not
quite as omnipotent as Client, but still meriting the big A
in mind and on paper.

P.A.G. probably has its own Premises department. This
would be staffed by specialists in building design and
construction, with expert knowledge of their company's
policies and needs. They would be responsible for
designing extensions and alterations at High Street
branches, and there would usually be a qualified architect
or two among them. But nobody's going to give a staff
architect his head with 20 storeys of onyx in the City of
London!

The Premises director is therefore instructed to check
with his senior staff and prepare a list of Architectural
practices considered to be most suitable for handling the
new project. They will be vetted by the Board, a polite
initial letter of inquiry drafted, and the 'Hunt' is on!

On receipt of the enquiry, each practice will delegate a
senior partner to try and win the appointment by whatever means he can. (Providing he's not seen to be in
blatant breach of R.I.B.A. protocol.) The senior partner
who wins the appointment for the successful practice is
deemed to be Architect – with the big A. He will pass
most of the detail and legwork to a team of minions
within the partnership and led by his 'first lieutenant',
the project architect – with a small a. But Architect is
'Captain'. It is he who goes on record as the originator of
the building and its features. To acquire that accolade, his
practice needs to fulfil one or more of the following
requirements if it wishes to be considered.

1. It is already known to the Board for its good work on an earlier project.
2. It is currently well reviewed in the glossy magazines for a magnificent monument recently completed.
3. It has been selected by the Board for submitting the best designs for the new building in a competition between firms invited to do so. (See Appendix A for information on Architectural competitions.)
4. It has recently taken out a comprehensive staff pension scheme with P.A.G. (probably on first getting wind of a big development job in the offing!).
5. Its senior partner plays golf regularly with the Chairman of P.A.G. and concedes a goodly percentage of two-foot putts.

Their various submissions are scrutinised by the Board: artistic impressions of the finished frontage with special features highlighted; the proposed layout of the ground floor and a typical upper floor; avant-garde design of the porcelain fitments in the director's loo; the suggested formula for calculating Architect's fees; and other equally vital factors. The Board assesses pros and cons, studies all the evidence placed before it, and pronounces judgement. The selected practice is then appointed and, subject to most other things being reasonably equal, number 5 in our list can be considered 11-to-8-on for the job!

His brief will be to spend no more than 48 months and £20 million, in converting a haphazard collection of old offices, warehouses, workshops and overgrown bomb sites, into 150,000 square feet of space-age office accommodation on 20 floors. With all four elevations clad in flamingo-tinted onyx!

Four years may sound reasonable but half that time will be spent seeking planning consents. Also wayleaves over and under other people's property for roads, electricity, gas, telephones, water and drainage services to be brought to the building. But as this book is about hunting – and not planning – problems, we'll leave those headaches where they belong – with Architect – and get on with the introductions.

Having introduced Client the father, and Architect the son, we now come to the third member of the holy trinity – Quantity Surveyor, the holy ghost! Although described in a more complex fashion in a later chapter, the following relates to his involvement in the 'Hunt' only.

A silent, seldom-seen deity with untold power. Dedicated to protecting Client's purse from predatory claims, nobody gets a penny until he authorises it.

His appointment could be on Architect's recommendation or Client's decision. But increasingly Client's, if Q.S. has his way. The research involved in preparing large Construction project more and more resemble a Cambridge Senior Wrangler paper, due largely to more and more mathematical factors introduced by Q.S. Like borrowing costs, alternative returns on capital for different ways of doing the development, rack-rents for possible tenancies, allowances for inflation, cash-flow, penalties, claims and counterclaims.

All too often a chartered accountant chairs the Board of big conglomerates today. Q.S. hunts Client with the 'ploy' that his interests are far better served by direct engagement of a fellow-'numbers' man – himself – than leaving it to Architect to find him one.

With the result that, especially on Management projects, of which more later, a lot more of Client's money is spent – directly and indirectly – on monitoring the value of work done, and close counter-monitoring of the monitors, than might otherwise have been the case.

That's probably one of the reasons why, on so many Management sites today, you'll see three blokes carrying coloured ball-pens, note books, measuring sticks and calculators, for every bloke carrying a hod of bricks!

To get back to P.A.G.'s project, Q.S. plays a part in the building design long before Architect's final working detail become part of the tender documents. It is he who analyses every innovation – and the more conventional bits above and below the ground – reducing them to fundamental materials-and-labour units. These units are then costed from his 'bible'. *The Surveyor's Manual of Pricing Schedules,* or some such title with the proprietary name of its publisher on the front of it.

It is a thick trade reference work of several hundred pages, updated annually, in which every possible combination of labour and material that go to make up a building, is priced per unit length, piece, volume, or area. From pile-driving a 20-inch diameter steel tube into London clay, or bedrock, or shale, or any combination of underground elements forming the sub-strata of our city, to laying a 20-foot diameter circle in 3-inch wide white mastic for a helicopter landing pad on the flat roof. Everything to be poured, laid, spread, fixed, or hung, will be analysed, reduced to units identifiable from the bible, and tagged up with a theoretical cost.

Having put his 'bible' to good use and painstakingly costed out Architect's brain-child, a meeting of the 'holy trinity' is called, when Q.S. presents his estimated cost of the new P.A.G. building in detailed and analytical form. Client pays scant attention to the detailed analytical format. He takes one look at the bottom line, utters a loud scream, and falls to the floor – senseless!

But neither Architect nor Q.S. are exactly new to the game. They've been all through this sort of thing before. They pick him up gently, dust him off and, uttering soothing noises, get Client to swallow a little brandy; or black coffee, if he happens to be a devout Arab or Quaker. Anxiously watching the colour return to his cheeks, they return to the conference table once he seems strong enough to continue.

Client's seizure, of course, is induced by the astronomical amount of money Q.S. reckons will be needed, if Architect is allowed to go ahead with the magnificent palace he and Client have envisaged between them.

"HOW much!?"

Architect gets all churlish in the belief that Q.S. hasn't the soul to appreciate, let alone know how to price up, his avant-garde designs – features that were meant to be the talk of art and architectural circles for the next half-century.

Nevertheless he agrees to return to the drawing board and dream up a few cost-cutting changes. Client, in turn, is persuaded to review some of his earlier grand-design criteria. Like imported crystal chandeliers in the entrance lounge, and high lighting levels on all floors; excessive warmth for those months with an 'r' in them – and excessive 'coolth' for those months without; acoustic mufflers in all ceilings and partitions, whether necessary or not; luxurious finishes to walls, floors and ceilings; custom-built furniture in staff canteen; and other extravagances of a similar nature.

But the onyx cladding, the tasteful accoutrements for director's offices and dining rooms, the Chairman's penthouse suite complete with snooker table, gymnasium, sauna, and private lift, remain unchanged on the grounds that certain qualities of life need to remain inviolate from penny-pinching economies!

Q.S. and Architect get into a series of huddles before presenting another set of calculations for the 'dissecting table' at full summit level. If they still won't fit the budget formula, Client calls for yet a further round of scrimping and saving until the time arrives when he's ready to look that bottom line straight in the eye without flinching!

3

Over to Paganism!

Just as a little knowledge of the Bible proved useful for introducing the 'holy trinity' of the Construction 'Hunt', a full 'left turn' into Greek mythology will help get the rest of the cast into perspective.

So picture Client, all-powerful, sitting Zeus-like at the very peak of Mount Olympus. All-attentive and obedient at his right hand, sits Architect, and equally so, on his left, Quantity Surveyor. Immediately below them are the lesser immortals or second-division gods – the various engineering practices like civil, structural, heating ventilation and air conditioning, electrical – including alarms and communications. They, together with 'the trinity', will form the permanent establishment on 'Olympus'. There may be others like acoustics or landscaping, but they would be engaged for a fee if and when needed and be attached to one of the permanent deities.

The engineers would be responsible for planning the technical needs of P.A.G.'s project, preparing drawings and tender-documents for 'hunters' to bid for the work, and supervising quality and progress during installation. But all under overall discipline of Architect. It is not unknown for a single Engineering practice to offer several, if not all, of the technical consultancy services listed above. In such cases there would be specialists in each field with a separate department within that practice, and each would attend the 'summit' meetings when their particular field was under discussion. And each of these specialist immortals will expect to be 'hunted' and sought after by devout worshippers – like manufacturers and

"I do wish they'd go away!"

sub-contractors – bowing and scraping at the foot of the mountain!

To reach that envied position on the 'Olympian' heights, those lesser immortals would have done a fair share of 'hunting', too. Consultants now 'hunt' for business openly. Professional bodies have abandoned 'holier-than-thou' policies that would once have 'de-frocked' a chartered consultant if he dared descend to marketing his services in a vulgar business-like fashion. Items 1 to 5 of the 'Architect's charter' on page 8 would help decide their selection by Client, or recommendation by Architect, but the rarefied air on the heights of 'Olympus' is their objective and no stone will be left unturned in their efforts to reach it.

The 'Olympians', including Architect and Q.S., would serve Client by designing and supervising the construction of his building. Architect and Q.S. would be rewarded by an agreed percentage of the total cost of the project, engineers by an agreed percentage of that part of the project for which they are responsible.

The ruling bodies of all eminent Consultants once laid down a rigid scale of percentages on which to base fees. These were geared to the size and complexity of a project, but were meant – in theory – to prevent one member from undercutting another when hunting for an appointment. In this way – in theory – the one-man practice produced a similar set of figures to the multi-partnered conglomerate, when each was asked for a schedule of proposed fees and ancillary charges.

But if the price was to be the same, and, to use a hunting analogy, – who could blame Client, the 'Master of the Hunt', from preferring to ride with a suave 'hunter from the Quorn', superbly mounted on a thoroughbred chaser and elegantly clad in Gieves-cut pink, in preference to an anxious, hollow-eyed rider astride a livery hack and dressed in faded cardigan, jeans and 'trainers'?

However, the Monopolies Commission and the Office of Fair Trading put a stop to all that. Fees, nowadays, are inclined to be subjected to hard competitive bargaining, with the ruling bodies turning a blind eye to the alleged breaches of their once inflexible codes. The investigating committees were no doubt pressurised by the 'hollow-eyed' ones. They had long complained that the said codes were drawn up by the 'fat cats of the Quorn' to the express advantage of the 'fat cats of the Quorn'!

And the game becomes increasingly tough on those on the upper slopes of 'Olympus'. Clients now put Architects and engineers into the same cruel and competitive world in which contractors have had to find their way for so long.

Having established his fee structure, a consultant would claim a proportion of his fee for himself when certifying claims for monthly progress payments to contractors. But it wouldn't end there. He would list expenses incurred and expect reimbursement for each time he or any of his staff visited the site; or for any other travelling he might consider beneficial for the project.

Like a trip to Stoke-on-Trent to check the glazing of a quarry tile he proposed to use on the entrance lobby floor; or to Florida to see how an American architect he'd read about in one of the glossy magazines had achieved perfect symmetry on a Miami building similar to the one he was now designing!

And while the preparation of drawings was part of his duties, he would charge over and above his fees for the number of copies he had to make for distribution purposes.

A 'hard-nosed' Client today says, 'You know where the site is in relation to your office. If you're any good at your job, you should be able to calculate how many times you or any of your staff will need to attend that site – or anywhere else you might have to travel in connection with getting this building up. By the same token you must make it your business to find out just how many drawings you will need to produce, and how many copies of each will be wanted for passing around.

So when doing your sums on what fees you propose to

charge me for your services, just make sure you've included for all that before sending me your quotation. Because whatever figure you put on that bottom line is all I am ever going to pay you!'.

But, being a reasonable man, Client agrees that if it can be proved that Architect has incurred extra expense through second thoughts of Client after the original concept was in hand, then he'll agree to consider Architect's claim for more money. If it can be proved! And then, no doubt, on a time-scale rate that has had to be included with his quotation.

Once the 'immortals' have agreed their wheelin'-'n-dealin' contracts, 'Olympus' will echo with the rustle of detail paper, the rattle of calculators, and the whir of computers. The professionals are churning out the conditions, specifications, drawings, and bills of quantity, whereby the building can be wrapped up and presented as one big paper package. A very big and awe-inspiring paper package. It is impossible to say how much paper this job could use up, but here are some rough figures.

1. Architect's and Engineers' drawings, including re-issues to incorporate variations during the course of the work, could number 6,000.
2. Q.S. and Engineers' bills of quantity can run into 1,200 pages.
3. Specifications and conditions prepared by Architect, Q.S. and Engineers can run to another 1,200 pages.

Print runs on items 2 and 3 would be about 50 sets of each; and it is not unusual for as many as 25 copies of each drawing to be required for distribution purposes.

Taking those 6,000 P.A.G. drawings to have an average area of 8 square feet; and an A4 sheet of paper to be three-quarters of a square foot; then the area of paper used to provide the basic needs of the project would be somewhere in the region of one-and-a-half-million square feet.

Then there are the thousands of in-house letters, memos, sketches, cost sheets and the like between

"Now that's what I call a paper mountain!"

personnel in the 'hunting' camps of the potential partici-
pants; and the thousands of informative and abrasive
bits of correspondence circulating among the appointed
ones. With a list as long as your arm on the bottom of each
– especially the abrasive ones – naming the people to
whom copies have been sent. That could easily account
for another million square feet of paper.

I make that a total of about 280,000 square yards, which
in round figures comes to a little under 60 acres.

Sixty acres should be enough to put a paper canopy
over the full width of the River Thames stretching from
Westminster down to Blackfriars Bridge; or eight thick-
nesses of cladding around the 600-foot high NatWest
Tower in the City of London; or swathe the slopes of
Mount Olympus seven times over!

Once the 'Olympians' have converted enough paper into
sets of tender documents, they're ready to make contact
with their 'mortal' worshippers; those contractors and
suppliers grouped around the foot of the mountain,
patiently seeking some sign of grace and favour from the
particular 'God' most likely to grant it in their case.

A devout 'hunter' will leap at the chance of paying
homage to his favourite immortal with a traditional burnt
offering. Well, not exactly a burnt offering – more medium
rare, and rinsed down with a good, chateau-bottled claret!

But it's all good for the project and should be encouraged.
Any social rapport he can achieve puts the 'hunter' on his
mettle, whereby he is honour-bound to perform well if
given the chance. It also helps the 'Olympian' to assess
the calibre of his pursuer.

Principal 'hunter' among immortals in pursuit of a
P.A.G. appointment has already been introduced as
Architect – and principal among mortals, once successful,
will become chief executive of the whole project. He gives
his name to the title of the next chapter.

4

The Main Contractor

For a concept as large, complex and prestigious as P.A.G.'s new H.Q. the trinity would seek an equally large and prestigious firm of builders. I am given to understand that there are probably not more than 20 in the south-east of England with sufficient resources and experience of large developments in the teeming City of London. Depending, once again, on how they measured up to items 1, 2, 4, and 5 in the 'Architect's Charter' on page 8, any number up to 12 would be approached in the first instance.

Five contenders should be enough to get down to reasonably competitive prices, but the 'Hunt' has been on for some time with a lot of introductions and hospitality bandied about. It's not too easy to show indifference to last month's hosts at Ascot, Lords, or Sunningdale!

A preliminary letter will be sent to each, asking if their current commitments will allow them to prepare a serious bid for the project; on the basis that say, eight weeks will be allowed for tendering, and two years for completion if successful. A brief description and some sketches will accompany the letter, which could be regarded as an invitation to apply for a 'Hunt-membership form'.

Applicants will be asked to present themselves for interview by the 'trinity', when many searching questions will need to be answered. Based on the replies, the field will be reduced to five or six. To each of these 'survivors' will be sent about half a hundredweight of tender documents, wherefrom they should be able to ferret out sufficient information to prepare a firm bid. Estimating personnel will pore over them for weeks, calculating prices against the thousands of items in the bills. Many are repetitive, but they each need to be priced and sub-totalled.

At first, they would use similar works of reference to Q.S. in pricing the bills of quantity, but then put their professional expertise to work in studying drawings and descriptive detail to find ways of cutting corners. If those corners are cut accurately and well, a 'hunter' would hope to put together a set of figures and terms that might win him the job; with sufficient margin for a small pot of gold for his shareholders – and a large smile from the Inland Revenue!

At the specified time the sealed bids would be opened with the Architect, Q.S. and sometimes Client, in attendance. Then follows a series of huddles when the merits and peculiarities of the respective bids, and bidders, are analysed. When two or more have bottom lines that look promising and fairly close to each other, their figures will be double checked – just in case somebody's left something out that he might want to claim more money for at a later date. Then they'll each be called in, separately of course, for long talks about finance, site-staffing, starting and finishing dates, assurances, insurances, and other admin. matters; besides agreeing any grey areas about the practical side of putting up the building.

But it is not exactly unknown for the bottom line on the lowest bid to be way over the top of what Q.S. told Client his new office block was going to cost, which puts Client on the verge of another attack of the 'screamin' hab-dabs'!

There is usually a choice of two alternatives in such cases. The 'Olympians' could go back to square one and re-vamp the job on more austere lines for another round of bidding. But that's going to take up more valuable time without knowing whether it'll succeed in bringing the price down to something acceptable. More often they'll call in the lowest tenderer(s) – separately again, of course, if more than one – and tell them that, although they may think they're running somewhere near the front of the 'Hunt', they're also running about a quarter of a million pounds over budget. If still interested in the job, what sort of modifications would they suggest be made to allow what savings to be made where, and resulting in what final figure?

Each builder's 'think-tank' goes to work. Their suggestions are itemised, individually priced, and submitted with a revised tender figure. The various alternatives are weighed in the balance by the 'Olympians' and a decision is reached. The successful (or perhaps by this time the not-so-sure-of-being-so-successful) builder is called in for a final ways-and-means meeting, at the end of which he should leave with the official appointment and title: Main Contractor for the P.A.G. 20-storey edifice. (If there's been a hard cost-cutting exercise from the beginning, Client may well have chopped two storeys out by the time the appointment is made!)

On hearing the good news, Main Contractor's first reaction will be to throw a 10ft high close-boarded hoarding right round the site and erect, in the most prominent position, visible proof of his triumph: a 100 square-foot freshly painted, massively built board; with his company name and identification logo taking up at least a quarter of its surface. The remaining area will be split up into a number of small rectangles. The names of the 'Olympians' will appear in the larger boxes and some of the principal sub-contractors who 'hunted' successfully in smaller ones, but usually only after agreeing to pay Main Contractor a rental charge for the resultant publicity!

That's the easy bit done. Now comes the real challenge. From an 'Olympian' thesis, comprising millions of lines and words set out on thousands of bits of paper, he's got to make a three-dimensional monument with all sorts of gimmicky goodies tucked inside it – some so novel and experimental that this will be the first building to put them to the test. Yet he's agreed to a crippling financial penalty should he not get the job finished by the agreed time. Not just the structure – but all the interior fixtures and fittings too. To cover himself he'll insist that any nominated supplier or sub-contractor whose performance could be vital to his programme, must accept a similar penalty from him before they can expect his order, no matter how keen their product or price, or who nominated them.

So even if he's succeeded in his own particular Hunt, a nominee might find that he's got to indemnify the builder for about £25,000 a week before he can expect that order he wanted so badly; the sum in question to be paid over if it can ever be proved that his non-delivery of, say, the boardroom cast-brass door-handles, made the building late for hand-over!

But as far as those sitting on top of 'Olympus' are concerned, it is Main Contractor who has to answer for everything and everybody physically connected with the job.

The front-runners of the 'Hunt' have now been introduced in traditional sequence and seniority. Between them they'll work hard to give Client the building he was after: Architect taking care of visual designs and cosmetic finishes both inside and out, engineers controlling foundations, structural framework, roads, sewers, and all technical services, main contractor in charge of all site activity, with Q.S. sitting on Client's wallet and fending off all sorts of predatory claims.

Yet main contractor has little say in Architect's decisions involving the cosmetics of the building: like whose onyx cladding, or windows, or sanitary ware, or ironmongery, or ceilings, or doors, or floor coverings will be used; a lot of which involving teams of specialist fixers on site to work under M.C.'s discipline. Nor is it any different in the case of Engineers' decisions over whose piling, or concreting, or steelwork, or lifts, or boilers, or chillers, or luminaires, or alarms, or gas, water, drainage, and electrical equipment to employ. Many of which again coming with their own site-installation teams.

But he does have to issue their orders and variations as instructed from time to time by Architect, monitor performance and progress on-site to minimise conflict between trades, deal with their claims for progress payment and send off his cheques within the stipulated time after applications are certified by Q.S., even if he himself has not yet received Client's cheque for the month in question. For all that, he is allowed 2½% of all payments to sub-contractors who, in order to allow for this deduction, add 1/39th to their calculations when quoting.

Since World War II, builders have grown considerably in size, strength, and financial muscle. Many feel that relying on the grace and favour of architects and quantity surveyors is no longer their rightful place in the 'Hunt'. They believe that, with all their knowledge and practical experience of the pitfalls and delays brought about by having 'theorists and artists' in charge, the main contractor should be one of the project team dealing direct with Client – not jumping through hoops at the whim of the 'Boys from Olympus'; and being blamed in his absence for the inevitable 'cock-ups'.

Resulting from this, it is now commonplace for leading builders to make direct approach to would-be Clients, pointing out the advantages of dealing direct with the only practical person, claim the builders, who know all the procedures and pitfalls of construction. They offer to provide all the professional design services or, alternatively, to help such professionals as are engaged by Client with the practical expertise they so badly need.

'We're there to be used!' is the cry, 'don't put months, if not years, on the length of your programme – and possibly millions on the cost – by making us subservient to your architect as of yore. There are a number of contract packages we can offer you that will put you and our project team together from concept to completion. And you, Mr Client, will benefit handsomely from the one we agree between us will best suit your needs.' (Another 'hunting' ploy?)

These contract packages come under the heading of 'Management Contracting', the principal versions of which are described in Appendix B.

5

Back to the Madding Crowd!

Main Contractor is newly appointed and has announced the fact to all-and-sundry with a 100 square-foot name board erected above his 10-foot high close-boarded site enclosure. The scene is now set for 'hunting' to begin in earnest. By the time the building is complete, some 150 to 200 specialist sub-contractors and suppliers will have won a nomination by Architect or one of the consulting engineers.

Architect will want to decide whose grade and shade of onyx should clad the outside walls between whose windows and decorative mullions; whose porcelain basins and pans go into the loos; whose handles go on whose doors; whose carpeting goes on whose patent flooring. Think of an average modern building, both inside and out, and visualise how many similar decisions need to be made.

Many of them, involving unimportant areas or where choice of material doesn't matter, are left to the main contractor – but where the visual effects of his artistry, colour consciousness, or imagination are to be on show, no self-respecting architect would dream of allowing others to decide for him. He'll want to see any number of samples of patterns and colour ranges from six or eight pottery firms, before he gives a decision on whose tiles go round whose urinals in the executive toilets. And he'll go through it all again when it comes to similar places elsewhere in the building.

In the same way, the various engineers will want to check on the plus and minus points of technical equipment on offer from scores of 'hunters' pursuing them. The Heating and Ventilation Engineer will do some in-depth research on whose boilers, valves, ducting, radiators, thermostats, fans, diffusers he's going to build into his designs – and which firms he'd like to have tender for installing them.

Just as the electrical engineer will want to talk to lots of people concerned with making and selling transformers, switchboards, lifts, alarm systems, light fittings, telephones, computer systems, etc – and once again which firms are to compete for putting them in. Structural engineers will do similar exercises, as will the civil and landscape people where applicable.

The installing firms, once appointed, will be responsible for ordering the specified equipment from the chosen suppliers and, in the end, as already stated, there could well be 150 firms so specified. Bearing in mind that between two and ten firms might compete for each of those 150 places, the full chase can consist of well over a thousand 'hunters', each 'Tally-ho!'-ing like crazy at the sight of an 'Olympian'. The foot-hills around that majestic peak might well resemble a crowd scene from *Ben Hur*!

But that's not the end of the story.

Augustus de Morgan, mathematician and scientist, wrote a well-known jingle about a hundred years ago.

'Big fleas have little fleas upon their backs to bite 'em;
And little fleas have littler fleas, and so *ad infinitum*!'

That could well be said about the Construction industry today. For instance, an electrical contractor seeking inclusion on the tender list for a big job, will be 'hunted' by suppliers of cable, conduit, trunking, switchgear, accessories; each offering attractive terms for their products to be considered when doing his calculations. My firm made lighting and electrical distribution equipment. No sooner did we start trying to get into a 'Hunt' for a big project – like P.A.G. – than word would get around and we'd be approached by various manufacturers and stockists of the parts we might need. All would offer privileged terms if we'd show preference for their goods when doing our sums.

Their sales personnel closely monitor the sequence of events in the main 'Hunt'. So closely, they sometimes know the outcome of the bit that concerns you before you learn of it yourself. I've had a supplier ring to ask when did I plan to place my order with him, as he'd just heard through the grapevine that we'd been appointed to the project in question. We'd heard nothing ourselves, despite having kept a pretty close ear to the ground. But sure enough, on checking with the 'Olympian' responsible for our involvement, I was told that the decision had been made at a meeting held only late that afternoon.

Assuming there could easily be a dozen of these 'littler fleas' to each of the 1,000 'little fleas' in the main 'Hunt', we've now got a mental picture of about 10,000 riders whoopin' and hollerin' across the field of vision. Compared with this, the portrait *The Charge of the Light Brigade* by Charles E. Stuart would appear as action-packed as *Whistler's Mother*!

But wait a minute! That's not really a true picture. Many would-be suppliers to nomination seekers would be common to a number of them. Manufacturers and merchants of non-specified materials would seek out as many as possible of those girding themselves up for the 'Hunt', and whisper to each the same 'honeyed' preferential terms. No doubt they would be just as 'honeyed' and preferential as those whispered to the seeker's competitors, but it means that there's probably only about six or seven thousand now in that secondary charge. Nevertheless, that's still about ten times as many as there were at Sebastopol, according to Tennyson!

The expressions, 'little fleas' and 'littler fleas', when referring to respectable businesss houses, are used as hyperboles to illustrate a point, and are in no way meant to be disparaging. None are parasitical, and many of the firms so irreverently described can well be many times larger than the 'quarry' whose business they're pursuing.

Up on 'Olympus', the project team are busy conferring,

drawing plans, doing sums, testing soils, scaling models, and all the other things that occupy a project team when designing an onyx-clad 20-storey office block in the City of London. While so doing they are inundated with a never-ending stream of visiting mortals displaying samples of their wares and anxious to indulge in a little social intercourse at any nearby up-market hostelry.

This doesn't just apply to the leading members of the project team. Their lieutenants, sub-lieutenants, secretaries and junior ranks are lobbied continually and find they have many kind and generous friends. Invitations to race meetings, golf tournaments, concerts, fashionable eating places and girlie clubs abound as tender lists are drawn up and the time approaches when each fortunate applicant is chosen. Once the fortunate 150 are identified, the hospitality wanes and it's 'back to the drawing board' for the remainder until the 'first smoke' from the next project is 'spotted on the horizon'. But the fortunate will still need a sympathetic ear and friendly hand when making claims for variations or seeking favour in a dispute, and therefore persevere with paying homage to their particular deity through the duration of the project.

But, in the end, inclusion on a tender list and award of a contract is rarely achieved by just being a good host and knowing a vintage Lafitte from a cash-and-carry 'plonk'! A good track record of comparable work previously executed is a must before your price can be taken seriously. No consultant is going to get egg on his face by having to explain to Client – at a top-level 'inquest' on what went wrong and how you were ever allowed to put in a price in the first place – that he found you great company, with an inexhaustible fund of dirty stories, and on first-name terms with the bouncer at the Eve Club!

Therefore, after the tenders have been scrutinised and the bottom two or three double-checked, similar questions are asked as those put by the Bench before passing sentence on some guilt-laden prisoner: 'What is known of this man?'. Well, they'd hardly ask that if the lowest happened to be somebody like G.E.C. or Pilkington Glass. But if you're neither of those, they may want to be sure you're capable of handling your slice of the cake, and that you'll stay in business long enough to finish the job for the price you've put in. Never mind if you go 'skint' the day after!

So if the scrutineers find too big a discrepancy between the lowest and the next, the former may well be disqualified on the grounds that somebody's blundered. It matters little if a contractor or supplier loses money because he misread a spec, or a drawing, but they don't want him looking for loopholes or lodging false claims once he discovers his 'cock up'. Nor do they welcome the embarrassment of his going out of business half-way through the job because, due to his unrealistic price, he's now run out of funds.

On the other hand, he could get a polite suggestion that he might like to re-check his figures. What a quandary that creates. Knowing from experience that this means he's probably the lowest, but by possibly too big a margin, he sets out on an exercise of logical analysis. 'We're too low,' he tells his team, 'but if we put our figure up, how much higher can we safely go and still remain the lowest? And having submitted a new figure what can we say was overlooked or miscalculated to explain the price change? And then we run the risk of disqualification on the grounds that the price we now ask was not the one submitted at tender date.'

The latter point is a valid one. Prestigious projects must be seen to be run strictly according to the established code. The option to re-check figures is intended to allow a tenderer to withdraw his bid before an order is placed. It does not mean that, having hit a coconut with a well-aimed throw at the fair, he is then asked if he'd like to change it for a bigger one!

On the other hand, those on 'Olympus' sometimes lend a sympathetic ear, especially to the 'two-foot-putt conceders'! Providing it was still the lowest, the revised estimate could still be accepted as valid if the reason given for the incorrect original was plausible enough. Like two cost-book sheets stuck together and read as one, or a floppy-disc failure on the recently installed computer which nobody really understands how to work. (A computer is now recognised as basic equipment in any business larger than that of an itinerant window-cleaner. Executives and senior staff resent not knowing the first thing about them and therefore delight at any alleged stupidity laid at its door.)

While weighing the pros and cons of changing his bid, the tenderer in question might try to have a word with those in charge to test reaction should he decide to do so. On learning that it would probably lead to his disqualification and loss of the job he chased so hard to get, he makes his decision.

'Having carefully checked my figures, I am quite satisfied with the price I quoted,' he states boldly. 'If there is any marked discrepancy between mine and those of my competitors, it is probably because I buy more keenly than they, have more competent and conscientious operatives, and personally supervise our performance throughout the project.' Or similar rhetorical, well-rounded line-shooting clichés. Never believed, but generally accepted as standard 'face-savers'.

The moment of truth arrives when he is awarded the much sought-after contract, and learns for the first time what sort of prices the opposition put in. It's hard to find words to describe how quickly the 'sweet smell of success' can change into the 'pungent pong of putrefaction', when he finds that he could have added another 'arm-and-a-leg' to his bid and still remained low enough to have won the job. But he has to put on a bold front and live with it – forever searching for means of cutting corners and claiming for variations, factual and fictional, to help take the hollowness out of his victory.

Victory in 'Site'!

Talking on this subject with an old architect friend over a researching lunch, he recalled a development project about 20 years ago in the City of London. After a keen struggle on a competitive basis the main contractor was appointed. It was a firm called Tersons – a large powerful organisation but not very long established. Their brief history is an interesting one.

When the ideological Labour Government decided, in their infinite wisdom, to form British Road Services by nationalising the long-haul carriers of private enterprise back in 1947, one of the biggest and oldest in that field was Carter Patersons. After nationalisation, and being left with but local work to do, the Board of C.P. decided to venture into the good old Construction industry – from the thick end. By taking the end syllables from their surnames they created Tersons. Their bought-in experts – head-hunted from the big old-established firms – decided the only way to instant greatness was to bid for everything and cut prices to the bare bone. By dint of high-pressure big-game 'hunting' techniques there was no shortage of opportunity. Once appointed, little time would be wasted in putting tender documents and site progress under the microscope, in pursuit of the flimsiest of excuses to claim more money.

With regard to the City of London project, my friend told me of the day he called the first site meeting. That's the one where those responsible for getting the building up, together with those who planned it, meet each other – often for the first time – and receive an encouraging pep-talk from Architect aimed at unifying the assembly into a purposeful team. Sitting round the table there would usually be principals from 'Olympus', main contractor, and the major sub-contractors. Whereas each of the planners might decide to have a partner or an assistant present, the 'doers' would usually send their project executive only. After all, it's really just the introductory 'summit' meeting between the operational bosses of the job.

When Architect went round the table for each in turn to identify himself, his firm, and his job responsibility, Tersons had no less than five: project manager, assistant project manager, site agent or general foreman, claims surveyor, and claims manager!

Something like a visiting centre forward bringing his personal manager, secretary, witness and lawyer into the dressing room for the pre-match tactical pep-talk by his team manager. He's already made up his mind that he's going to be fouled four times in the second half!

Mind you, Tersons operated just as ruthlessly the other way, too. Their surveying team, laughingly known as the bloodsucking brigade, would be forever searching for counter-claims against their sub-contractors – alleging site damage and delays whereby authorised payment could be withheld or reduced. That's from personal experience.

Inevitably they fell apart, went into liquidation, and – just as inevitably – put countless hard-working sub contractors and suppliers into dire straits, paying a few coppers in the £ against the several millions owed in unpaid debts.

The moral? Winning jobs with oversharp pencils, followed by abrasive claims against all and sundry, butters no parsnips!

Back now to the P.A.G. project.

By the end of the main and secondary tendering stages, some 200 individual sub-contractors and suppliers will have been appointed, Architect having instructed main contractor in writing that orders be placed with the successful firms in question. They will be told to proceed in accordance with the tender documents and quotation, and to comply with the terms and conditions of the project. There will also be the small print on M.C.'s order form, which is well worth a lot of close scrutiny. Many impose conditions regarding penalties, use of plant, and method of payment, that are often harsher and more in main contractor's favour than those set out in the tender documents. It's then up to the firm in question to tell main contractor that he's pushing his luck; and then to fight for better terms. Nobody wants delays while 'small-print' is being squabbled over, so right should triumph if it persists.

That Architect's Instruction is the all-important piece of paper in the industry and marks the end of the 'Hunt' as far as a specific trade or product is concerned. The chase is over, the spoils have gone to the victor, and those that hunted in vain must accept defeat quietly and look elsewhere for another 'Olympian' challenge.

Mind you, with six to eight people competing each time – and averaging something like one win to every half-dozen losses, it was not surprising that seasoned 'hunters' got cheesed-off with accepting defeat and looked around for ways of beating the system; a system in which each set of tender documents included an undertaking, to be signed by somebody high up in the tendering firm, that there had been nothing even remotely akin to collusion with any other bidder in preparing its price for the job. Nevertheless, there were seasoned 'hunters' who believed that a bit of good, old-fashioned colluding, was much to be preferred to beating brains out against other 'brain-beaters', and took their chances in a methodically unlawful fashion.

Some of the methods they used are described in Appendix C, under the heading of 'Pack-hunting!'.

6

How to be a Victor

With the example of a typical appointment of one of possibly 200 nominated suppliers and sub-contractors, each to play some part in the P.A.G. project, we enter the last chapter of Part One. A victor has emerged and an order is about to be placed.

Those two magically therapeutic words – An Order! How brightly the sun shines and how sweetly the birds sing when that long-hoped-for flimsy piece of paper arrives with the morning mail. The chase was so long and so hard, and so often were you on the verge of 'baling-out' of the competition when it looked as though the cards were stacked against you. But you won through.

Let's see if it's possible to establish a formula for winning.

The immediate answer is – 'Well, that's easy. Just put in a keener price than anybody else!' But that's not all of it. Sometimes a job is negotiated with one favoured nominee only. You, naturally, want to be that nominee, to the exclusion of others who might be even better at what you do than you claim to be. If that, of course, were really possible! Or if a single nomination is not negotiable, you'll settle for being one of a short-listed half-dozen out of maybe 20 or more trying to get on a tender list. The big question in any race with a field of 20 or more, is just when to make your final challenge.

To bid for a job and lose it over price or delivery is disappointing, but honourable. Not to be asked to bid, despite all your efforts to get on that tender list, is humiliating, to say the least. You look at the names of those who were asked, or as many of them as your source of information will divulge, and comment bitterly that it seems to be the same old names and faces that get the chance on the 'big ones'. Yet if you could get down to some in-depth research on the subject, you'd probably find it was because they used applied psychology and did some sound marketing at the right time. 'Fine,' I hear somebody say, 'but when's the right time?'

Apply too early on the consultant's telephone, or at his office, and his secretary comes on to tell you that he's tied up all day with meetings, but he did tell her to say that if it was about the P.A.G. job you're far too early anyway. It's going to be at least another six months before structural and technical designs are sufficiently advanced for tender documents to be prepared for the bit in which you're interested.

You make a note in your diary to get in touch again about five months later. But then you remember that your competitors have also had their ear to the ground, and no doubt were told much the same as you when making their enquiries. They, too, probably have diaries in which they make similar notes. So, being a sharp cookie, you don't wait that full five months – you're in his front office all bright and breezy with scarcely four-and-a-half months ticked off in that diary since your last visit. Out comes your man, equally bright and breezy, and you spend the next 20 minutes chatting about ships, and string, and sealing wax, and holidays, and golfing feats, etcetera, until you tentatively put out your first feeler: – 'How are your designs on the P.A.G. project coming along in relation to programme – and why don't we go out and talk about it over some lunch?'.

Your friend expresses surprise that you didn't know it went out for pricing seven weeks ago, and that it was only last week that an order was placed with the successful tenderer – who also happens to be your most unpopular rival. Unpopular with you, that is. Salt is then rubbed into the wound with, 'Why didn't you tell us you were interested? Your name would have gone on the tender list without question, and we might even have tried to help you a little. After all, you performed excellently on the last job we did together, and I for one would have been glad to have seen you on this one!'

The salt would have done you a lot more good had you used it right; like taking it with the tale about it being six more months before anybody was ready to talk to you about the job. Consultants expect to be pursued, but try to reduce the field by putting down a false scent. There's a limit to the amount of high-cholesterol lunches a man can digest in a week, and the more gullible people he can get to go away and keep away for as long as possible, the greater his chances of being on target with his duties to the design team.

Design teams get priorities wrong under pressure, and then panic to get a specialist sub-contractor or supplier appointed when there's a risk that main contractor is sharpening his pencil in anticipation of a claim for delays. It means that six months yesterday can easily become six weeks tomorrow.

Or it could be that simplified documents are decided upon at an early stage in the programme to get some of the sub-contractors started earlier, Client having just found an overseas company that wants to lease the top six floors at a good rent; the only proviso being that the place must be ready for them to move in three months earlier than the original completion date. In such cases Consultants might be told to seek and negotiate with one firm, rather than spend time completing specifications and drawings to a stage at which half-a-dozen can squabble over it. The possible increased cost to Client of a non-competitive deal is more than offset by a fat rent roll flowing in three months ahead of schedule.

In other cases a 'carrot' would be offered to those already contractually involved. 'Increase your work force,' they will be told, 'and bring forward delivery of your materials – and a specified sum or percentage will be

37

added to your contract figure by way of an acceleration bonus.'

But just as the Town Hall at Hamelin played hard-to-get with the Pied Piper's fee once he'd completed his part of the contract, it's amazing how a Client will find ways of ducking out when asked to meet a promise of acceleration bonuses. After all, he'll protest, even if 199 contractors have flogged themselves successfully to meet what's been asked of them, it's no use to him if the lift-, or lighting-, or flooring-, or window-people are still dragging their heels.

Be that as it may, those taking part in a Construction 'Hunt' should never slacken pace and relax. Those folks up there on 'Olympus' are not like you and me: they tend to do the most unpredictable things the moment your back's turned!

Only 'hunters' with muscle, charisma, luck, or a fortuitous foot in the door at the right time, can expect to be included when the names go into the hat. So having got known – stay known! Be gregarious. Get around. Get away from that desk and visit people.

Much-soured losers often mutter darkly about mystic bonds between consultants and their so-called favourites. Like Freemasonry, membership of the same church, or synagogue, or golf club, or old boys' network. But there's nothing mystic or sinister about belonging to as many chummy little communities as possible. In fact, it's to be highly recommended – even if one or two might border on being a bit of a closed shop. There's nothing cosier than being locked in with the membership of a closed shop, looking out on the envious peering in through the window. And if you don't happen to be a Catholic, or a Jew, or a golfer, or an Old Wykehamist, there's always such things as affiliate, associate, or honorary memberships. Most social institutions need more funds in these expensive times. Which is why they tend to fall over backwards in encouraging applications for social or associate

"No asphalting wanted today, thank you."

membership to help swell the ranks – and, of course, the coffers. Without imposing too many stringent conditions to daunt a would-be-joiner.

So take advantage of the situation – be a joiner! Invest a few hundred quid a year in taking up membership of as many different groups as you can afford to join. I'm not talking about your trade associations – you'll get no business out of them! At least, not until you've been a member for 20 years and have worked your way into the inner circle at the top – where first-hand knowledge of useful leads get passed around long before they're made known to rank-and-file members.

Nor do I mean that, having wangled yourself membership of the Athenaeum, you walk into a lounge filled with bishops and learned judges, waving a fistful of business cards, and enquire in a stentorian voice if anybody's looking for a reliable firm of asphalting contractors. Even if you have left your foreman keeping the tar-pot on the boil by a parking meter in Pall Mall!

No, it's simply a matter of finding little bits of common ground that you find natural to share and enjoy with others. That's the key word – 'natural'. If you're one of those who mix naturally, then forget searching hard for what might be good for your business and do the natural thing. Get in there and enjoy yourself. The more people you meet and get on with socially, the greater the possibility of a chance encounter that will lead to a 'pole-position' in a good 'hunt'. (That's a slightly mixed metaphor designed to emphasise the point. And here comes another for the same reason.) It's a piscatorial fact of life that the more lines dangled in the water the greater the chance of a fish.

There's a quotation from an unknown source that sums up the subject nicely; 'A wise man knows everything; a shrewd one – everybody!'

To illustrate this point now follows a trilogy of personal experiences with a common theme, each of them describing how, when mentally and physically miles away from business pursuits and enjoying the company of others, one can finish up at the end of the day right up there in front of a big 'Hunt'. Not even 'hunting'! Just up there on 'Olympus' with exclusive negotiating rights – to the chagrin of all those that 'chased' away like mad, only to see the prize they wanted so badly, given to another.

Each story is complete in itself, although there are coincidental links. The common theme is:

Pleasure + People + Places = A worthwhile deal you don't otherwise get!

Although each has its own distinctive background, they weave themselves into a colourful background, with characters and places known to many.

The world of horse-racing provides the initial backdrop: after all, much of what is written here is strewn with terms of the turf. Like the 'Hunt', the 'Chase', the 'Field'. And as the objective of the book is to show how consultants, contractors and manufacturers are obsessed with getting specified for involvement in an 'Olympian' project, the first tale in the trilogy combines the two.

It tells the true story of a famous steeplechaser and Grand National winner named 'Specify', and how he lived up to his name in the context of the real meaning of the word – in no uncertain fashion!

PART TWO

How to Win Without Really Trying!

7

A Day at the Races!

In 1961, my business was spread over half a dozen small workshops, stores and offices in Holloway, North London. Not a very efficient arrangement. But having discovered golf a couple of years earlier, the magic of the game compensated for a lot of business difficulties.

I was drawn to play in an Eccentric Club knockout competition against a fellow member named George Williams. We hadn't met before and, as he lived in Thetford, Norfolk, we agreed to play our match one midweek morning in May, 1961, at a course about midway between our homes. As we walked round he told me about the overcrowded refrigeration engineering business he had run in northwest London until about a year before, when he moved into a brand new factory and three-storey office block in Thetford. It was the time when the London County Council (to become the Greater London Council in 1965) wanted to get industry and people out of overcrowded London, and offered magnificent facilities to encourage moves to designated expanded towns like Thetford.

Having agreed that the loser bought the lunch and the winner the wine, by the time we'd finished *his* second bottle of Chambertin, George had persuaded me to come up and join him for a game at Thetford a couple of weeks hence – with a view to looking at the options of moving my own outfit up there.

He was obviously a good talker, as were his friends, Ellis Clark, the Thetford Town Clerk, and Bill Jennings, the Borough Engineer and Planning Officer. The four of us golfed and lunched, after which I signed up for a 30 year lease on a 5,000-square-feet new factory at four shillings per square foot per annum! New houses were provided at low rents for our key personnel, who – together with plant, machines and stores – were moved to Thetford in August 1961. I kept the admin. and sales in London, from where I continued to operate; it only took 85 minutes to get to Thetford from my home in Cuffley, Herts.

For the next seven years I would commute two or three times a week, often staying overnight at The Anchor, a mock-Tudor pub on the banks of the River Thet, in the centre of the sleepy old town. Sleepy – that is – except for the juggernauts thundering over the narrow iron bridge to and from Norwich or King's Lynn; potential Grand Prix drivers practising chicane-turns while roaring to or from the motor racing at Snetterton; and endless caravanserais of trailers, boats and mobile homes being towed to and from the beaches of Yarmouth, Cromer and the Norfolk coast in general. The sleepy old features were restored when an inner-ring relief road was built about ten years later, taking the traffic round the outskirts of the town. An outer-ring dual carriageway, completely by-passing Thetford, has been on the drawing board these past 25 years, and may yet be built before the century ends.

The Anchor was my second home and social club, when working from Thetford, and good friendships were formed with mine host, other commuting mini-tycoons like myself, and one or two entrepreneurs of the 'homespun' variety. One of these was Paul Rackham, Thetford born-and-bred, and about 20 years my junior.

I first met him soon after moving up there, at which time he'd been working for himself something like 18 months. Before that he drove a bull-dozer for John Laing on round-the-clock shifts, when Laings were building the M1. When he saw that his home town was on a rapid expansion course, he left Laings, bought a second-hand JCB and bid for the clearance and levelling of a 20-acre virgin site – so that contractors could start to build the largest single factory complex in the development of Thetford as a modern industrial town. He won the job and worked day and night with his old JCB to make it pay. Handsomely!

His new enterprise went on to expand into a thriving earth-moving and plant-hire business, operating from a three-storey office block and workshops that he built for himself – with a number of satellite activities like construction, waste collection and disposal, and insurance broking. His business ventures grew faster than his cashflow, as happens to so many of us, and in 1966 he sold out for more than quarter of a million! That was five years after we had first met, and by which time we had become great friends.

We were both fond of racing and had good party days at some of the Yarmouth, Huntingdon and Newmarket meetings. When I stayed overnight during the summer, he and I would meet on the first tee of Thetford Golf Club at 6am for nine holes of golf, and then back to The Anchor for breakfast and champers on the loser.

In October, 1966, I bought a yearling in partnership with Paul at the Newmarket Autumn Bloodstock Sales, and raced him under my own colours as a two-year-old the following year. Paul already had three or four of his own in training, and kindly left all ownership decisions to me on this one. When it came to naming our purchase I decided on Bermuda Boy, having just got back from a memorable holiday there with my wife about a month after we'd bought him.

Bermuda Boy went to the stables of Newmarket trainer, Arthur Freeman who, seven or eight years earlier and putting up half the weight he currently had draped around him, had won the Grand National on Mr What. And among the 20-odd horses Arthur had in his training stables was a brown gelding, bred in eastern Norfolk from an ex-Scottish Grand National winner called Specific. The gelding's name was Specify.

An East Anglian farmer, Fred Rogers, who was also pretty big in building and property developing around Lowestoft, was the owner of Specify – having bought him as a yearling from the breeder in 1961. He now merits a place in our story.

Fred Rogers was a loveable old character and a great friend of Paul Rackham's. He had a 'carrot-crunching' Norfolk accent you could cut with a knife. Besides the old-established family business referred to in the previous paragraph, he also owned a few streets of houses and a farm or two in and around the Felixstowe area. Not to mention about half-a-dozen thoroughbred horses in training. I first met him in the Club bar at Yarmouth races, where a horse of Fred's, one of Paul's, and Bermuda Boy, were each running in different races. There wasn't a winner among them, but they all finished somewhere in the frame, which meant we did at least have a bit of prize money to come. Not that it was likely to change anybody's life-style!

Yarmouth isn't Ascot, and 20 years ago prize-money for having a horse placed would hardly cover the cost of the day's outing for an owner, by the time he's lunched his friends and bought a celebratory bottle or two. Especially after the trainer, the stable, and the jockey have had their bit! By tradition, Wetherby's are the sole rule-makers, book-keepers, accountants, and bankers to the thoroughbred-ownership world. All financial involvements to and from an owner, other than training fees and personal betting commitments, are handled by them – for a fee, of course – and at the end of each month a detailed statement issued. If the account is not comfortably in credit then a cheque is called for by return to make it so. There's a fixed minimum percentage due to a jockey, trainer, and stable staff, as a 'spontaneous expression of gratitude' if an owner comes into a bit of prize-money. And just in case anybody's a bit slow in showing their delight, 'big-brother' Wetherby takes care of the hand-out through its computer!

Being a farmer, Fred Rogers was never one of those 'jolly-Rogers'! He complained that what with the cost of training and having to pay his bookmaker when his horses lost – which they were inclined to do all too frequently, despite the trainer's assurance that this time the horse was so fit it could fall and break a leg a furlong out and still hobble in first – it meant sending off the title deeds of another house, or maybe two, to either his trainer or to Ladbroke's when he got back to the office, after a fun-day at the track!

He was 80 years old then, with an unruly shock of snow-white hair and a complexion that a lifetime of exposure to Anglian sun, winds and rain had weathered to the colour of a lightly boiled beet! Over the ensuing four or five years I must have been in his company a dozen times or more, but have never known him dressed any differently than he was at that first meeting. Bare headed with those white locks blowing in the wind, a khaki shirt with a red tie, a 'pepper and salt' Harris-tweed sports jacket, a pair of the most voluminous and longest khaki shorts I've ever seen, and khaki socks with their turnover-tops finishing an inch below his turnip-sized knees; and the whole ensemble handsomely shod in a pair of highly polished heavy brogue brown shoes. Winter or summer, in his office, at a race meeting, on a building site, or at a lunch reception, Fred never seemed to have a problem over what to wear today.

Whether he was running out of house-deeds or whether with *Anno Domini* creeping up he felt like opting-out of horse ownership, I don't know, but in 1969 Fred sold Specify to Paul Rackham for £6,000. Paul had the gelding moved to Derek Weeden's yard in Mildenhall, about 8 miles from Newmarket. At about this time Paul was speculating heavily in property development. He also owned and lived on a modern pig farm near Bury St Edmunds – where about 5,000 'boarders' lived out their 16 weeks in electrically heated-and-lit houses, without ever seeing the light of day or emitting the faintest unsavoury smell – and was heavily into show-jumping and displays, with some 20 or more good-quality horses housed in his farm stables.

He'd certainly come a long way since those swing-shift 'dozer-drivin' days on the M1 construction!

One morning in February 1970, Paul phoned to say he was just leaving Thetford with a few friends and how about joining him at Windsor races that afternoon, where Specify was due to run in the main event of the day – a three-mile steeplechase. I put the phone down and did some serious thinking. Up to my neck trying to run a business, it didn't seem right to ignore all that paper on the desk and set out, pleasure-bent, at the casual behest of a friend.

It was now three years since I sold out my Thetford interest, and a long time since Paul and I had last met. The best way out of the dilemma was to spin a coin. But it still took four spins before it came down right for Windsor that afternoon!

In the Members' enclosure I joined up with Paul, Fred Rogers, and Fred's inseparable companion, cheery Charlie Manning, an ex-Cockney fairground owner from Felixstowe. There were also one or two mutual friends from Thetford that had come down with the party. Unfortunately Derek Weeden had opted to go to another meeting in the North with a couple of other horses he trained, and therefore was not to be around on this fateful day to witness history in the making!

We discussed the pros and cons of Specify against the three first-class horses he was to race against, but with Terry Biddlecombe on his back he seemed well worth a gamble. Especially as the bookmakers had made him 7 to 1 outsider of the four. The previous race had already been won by an outsider, Cala Mesquida, owned by Fred Pontin, the holiday hotel 'king'. But as it had been my choice I now possessed good 'bookmaker's money' for a strong loyalty bet on Specify.

History would not have been made that day had not

Specify and Terry romped in three lengths ahead of the field.

Brimming over with elation (and winning Tote tickets) we stood in an excited group at the members' bar, reliving the race and dodging the flying champagne corks. Fred Pontin was the central figure of another happy champagne-quaffing group celebrating their good fortune just a little further along the bar. The two groups slowly merged into one. When he found that the talk about horses was becoming a bit too repetitive and technical, Fred explained, quite candidly, that he was not over-obsessed with horse-racing as a purist or pundit. He enjoyed ownership because publicity from his Turfing activities proved good for his business.

He went on to say how he envied Paul in having Specify already entered and qualified to run in the Grand National, due to be run at Aintree six or seven weeks later. After the day's performance against three other fancied runners down to run in that epic event, he had to stand a good chance of getting into the frame, and the resultant publicity would reflect well in the 'Go Pontinental!' image. Paul, about whom it has been said that he'd sell his grandmother providing the price was right, told Fred there was no need for any envy.

'For £16,000', said Paul, 'you can have Specify and run him in the National under your name, with your jockey wearing your colours. The only proviso being that you don't shift him to your trainer's stables until after the race, but allow him to stay with Derek Weeden. Derek's a good pal of mine and has never had the luck to train a runner in the National. I wouldn't like him to lose out on this deal. Also, after today, I believe that with the luck that any horse needs to complete the course, he might well win. In which case I shall want another £6,000 out of the tidy sum you'll pick up as the lucky owner.'

'O.K.,' replied Fred, 'they seem to be reasonable conditions and I agree to them. So I'll give you £10,000.'

The scene was set for a classic bout of time-honoured 'horse-trading'. A prospective buyer and seller of a desirable property had made contact and agreed terms. All that had to be decided was how much. More corks popped, glasses were freshened up, and free advice from both camps filled the air.

'You've got to be joking,' said Paul, 'but as a gesture of goodwill I'm prepared to give my horse away for the stupid price of £15,000.'

'I'm informed by my advisors,' observed Fred, 'that according to his form-book rating he's not worth the offer I made you, but because I'm keen on any horse wearing my colours in the National this year my final bid is £11,000. You'd better take it quick, son, because I think I must be crazy and half inclined to pull out without waiting for your answer.'

Paul didn't take it and Fred didn't pull out. Came pauses for more refreshment and tactical huddles in each camp. The asking and offering figures crept closer together. £14,000 and £12,000. And there they seemed to stick with nobody prepared to budge further. 'Right,' said one of Fred's party, 'split the difference and settle for 13.' 'Not on your Nellie!' was the general cry. 'What chance would the poor thing stand with an 'orrible figure like 13 forever hanging round its neck!.'

In the end they agreed to toss, 12 or £14,000. A member of Fred's party pulled a huge handful of mixed coins from a capacious coat pocket and, turning them over with a resounding crash on the bar counter, covered them as best he could with both hands.

'Call, somebody! he demanded.

'Tails!' cried Paul.

Breathlessly we watched as half-crowns, two-bob bits, shillings, sixpences, pennies and ha'pennies, not to mention those then-new twelve-sided, threepenny monstrosities, were carefully slid to one side or the other of the slowly diminishing central pile. There then remained one heap of coins, all 'heads', and another all 'tails'. Even more carefully each heap was counted. Then followed the solemn but irrevocable verdict.

"Now specify heads or tails!"

A Day at the Races!

'By 17 "heads" to 15 "tails", the horse Specify goes to Fred Pontin for £12,000!' On went the junketing.

We now approach the real reason for telling a Dick Francis-type story in the middle of a serious work of reference on the Construction industry. But before getting on to that I'll finish the Specify saga — there's bound to be a few readers with more than a passing interest in racing who may have forgotten its spectacular ending. Understandable, as it all happened in the early 1970s, and even some of the colourful coinage referred to above might be a bit puzzling to younger readers — whose pocketfuls of pees today count for so little compared to the so-called small — but oh-so-weighty — change of those days.

In the Grand National that year Fred Pontin ran Specify with John Cook on his back. He went well and was only about sixth when brought down by The Otter just four fences from home.

The following year he started at 28 to 1 in the same race, and having completed two full circuits, lay fifth after jumping the final fence. He seemed to have no chance of getting among the front runners on the long run-in, but John Cook went for the narrowest of gaps on the far rails as they approached the 'elbow'. Then, pushing the gallant Specify with might and main up the final one-and-a-half furlongs, he almost lifted him over the line to win the 1971 Grand National by less than half-a-length!

Fred decided that having achieved the greatest accolade of all, the champion deserved to rest on his laurels. He let Paul look after him down on his Suffolk farm, where Paul hunted with the horse in winter, and just let him rusticate and smell the flowers during the fine weather. After a couple more years he got a bit too stiff and rheumaticky for hunting (Specify, that is — not Paul Rackham) and Sir Fred Pontin — as he was by this time — took him back to enjoy a happy retirement in the grounds of his hotel in the Isle of Wight. And to the best of my knowledge that's where Specify ended his days — no doubt boring the bejasus out of any riding-school hack sharing his pasture, while the gallant old horse delivered yet again a fence-by-fence account of how he won the Grand National at Aintree in the Spring of 1971!

Back to Windsor on that bleak February afternoon. What with all the tumult and the shouting while the buying and selling was in progress, I don't believe anybody gave the slightest thought to the fact that there were three more races being run somewhere out there. We just stood about in groups opinionating on what had taken place. I remember commiserating with Paul over the two 'grand' he might have made had he called 'heads' instead of 'tails'.

'Well, let's get it right,' he replied. 'I only gave £6,000 for him a year ago, and sold him today for £12,000. I had a couple of nice touches with him earlier in the season, and there's today's prize money as well. I wouldn't mind doing a "one-horse" deal like this every year.'

'Besides,' he went on, 'I've just struck lucky on some land I bought in Felixstowe some time ago. That place is going to be *the* number one port if this country ever gets into the Common Market. Only this week I got planning permission confirmed to erect half-a-million square feet of speculative warehouse buildings on the site in three phases. Fred Rogers' firm is starting to level the ground for phase one next week, prior to getting on with the building.' A thought suddenly struck him. 'Say! What about coming down to next month's project meeting in Fred's office. You can meet the architect, pick up some drawings, and give us your expertise on electrics. We want them all fitted out with lighting, heating and power, in order to lease them off as ready-to-go as soon as they're finished. You can take care of all that, can't you?'

I could and I did. About two years later, my company – with the aid of a local firm of electricians to whom I sub-contracted the site installation work – had provided about 20,000 feet of our standard lighting trunking, and about

2,000 of our standard twin-tube luminaires. They were fitted into something like 30 smart-looking buildings, ranging from 10 to 30 thousand square feet in area, that were being bought up as fast as completed by those anxious to make the most of Britain's entry into Europe on 1 January 1973.

Monthly site meetings at Felixstowe were colourful affairs. I suppose I attended about six of them during the project. While they were in progress, Client – alias Paul Rackham – was the *enfant terrible* . . . 'in spades'! None were spared his scathing abuse as he pursued accelerated progress. But just as soon as the meeting was over all would adjourn to the Orwell Hotel, where maybe 16 or 20 of us would sit down to a magnificent lunch in a private dining room (fortunately they were pre-breathalyser days) and for which Paul would often pick up the tab. Sometimes, I must admit, only to look carefully round the table and toss it on to one of us with a, 'Come on, it's your turn, Morley', or Rogers, or Rodney, or whoever.

Rodney was Rodney Furze, senior partner of a Norwich firm of architects. He and I got to know each other quite well at those post site-meeting lunches, whereby further work came to my Company from other projects in which he was involved.

At the Eccentric Club of St James's, London, SW1, Alfred – the resident barber – used to hold court in his well-equipped saloon up on the second floor. That barber shop was almost a club within a club, as a member would arrive at his appointed time, or perhaps a few minutes early, and exchange pleasantries with the member in the chair once Alfred had completed the introductions and assuming they didn't already know each other.

I was in there for a haircut about a week after Windsor – in those days I believe there was a bit more hair to cut. Sitting in the chair was Fred Pontin. Although we'd both been members for several years I don't believe our paths had ever crossed before when using the Club. Little time was wasted in getting a bottle sent up from the lounge bar on the first floor, while we regaled Alfred with highlights of that great day at Windsor.

Coming to the end of the commentary I was asked what was my line of country, when not attending alfresco horse-dealing hooleys in Berkshire. When told, he asked if I had a business card for him to pass to his architect, who was always spending Fred's hard-earned cash in building new developments and improving old ones in the Pontin leisure empire. He said to get in touch with the man, whose name he gave me, if I hadn't heard from him within the next couple of weeks or so. He would drop the fellow in question a line, together with my card, once he got back to the office.

The rules of the 'Hunt' are simple. Having been presented with the gift of a valuable introduction, don't then wait for the other party to make the next move. I remember drafting a carefully worded letter when I got back to the office, touching lightly on Fred Pontin's recommendation that I get in touch. Believing that one should never send publicity enclosures with initial introductory letters to strangers, I said that literature describing my company, its products, and some of the prestigious projects for which we'd been specified (there's that word again!) would follow under separate cover within the next couple of days.

I am writing this in 1986 – four years after selling my business and retiring. Yet I believe my old firm still has the goodwill of that architectural practice to whom that letter went over 15 years ago.

And all because I played 'hookey' and went to the races one February afternoon in 1970!

There endeth the first lesson!

8

The Great Fire of Sandown!

The first part of this trilogy drew to a close with a scene in the barber shop of the Eccentric Club. I couldn't think of a better place to start the second one.

But first the clock needs to go back a couple of years. To the time when the Club president of the day – one Sir Malcolm Miller – decided that, situated as it was in the heart of prestigious St James's country, the Eccentric ought to have its own Magazine. With the result that a circular went out to the membership from the secretary's office, that Sir Malcolm would provide a handsome dinner for four in one of the best eateries in town to he who would inaugurate the scheme. There would also be tokens of appreciation, like a 'thank-you' note on 'Sir's' embossed heading, for those providing readable and interesting material for publication in the new venture.

I liked the idea of my Club pushing out its own image and wrote to the secretary. 'Having had an article or two accepted by *Punch* over the years,' I said, 'once you've found somebody to produce and edit all the build-up needed for a Club Magazine, I wouldn't mind trying my hand at a light-hearted contribution from time to time if wanted.' Or words to that effect.

Now we go back to the barber shop. It's the Spring of 1969 and I'm getting the full treatment about a month or so after my letter, when the secretary walked in for a chat. As was often his wont.

'How's the Magazine project coming along?' I asked, once the badinage had ceased on Alfred's masterly arrangement of such hair as was left on my over-exposed scalp (three either side of the parting and the centre one swept back). He thought long and hard, made a big play of counting up on the fingers of both hands, and then spoke:

'Well, adding up from memory and including your very nice letter, Mr Morley, up until today I've received one reply. We appear to have a right erudite lot in this Club!'

There was a sad, reflective pause, as, with half-seeing eyes, he watched Alfred put the finishing touches to his handiwork. Then, with spectacles steamed up with excitement, he exclaimed, 'Look, you're the only one to answer – why don't you produce the Magazine? You say you've got some experience of writing – it should be a doddle for you!'

We won't go into all the 'who – me?'s and 'you must be joking?'s, but at the end of the day I came out of that barber shop smelling like a million dollars and voicing the promise that I'd give it some thought.

The more I thought about it the more I fancied the challenge. After all, for many years now I had designed, written and published lots of colourful literature about how good my Company was at making what we did – and although many didn't believe half of what was written, nice things had been said about the *way* it was written. It was well on the cards that I'd get some kick out of writing, but fitting it in with all the other work-and-play activities could be a problem. Still, I'd have a go!

So for the next five years I'd burn the midnight oil well into the morning, both at home and at the office, churning out a 50 to 60 page *Eccentric Magazine* (50% reading matter – 50% advertising) twice a year. Much time was spent with the printers that did all my Company work: correcting galley proofs, deciding format and page layout, and pasting up, etc. both for reading and advertising matter. I had always spent a lot of money on publicity literature for my Company – well, a lot for one of our size – and the printers were more than co-operative in both time and charges for my latest hobby. I even got them to take, and pay for, a page of advertising in each issue, as I did for my own business. The result was that the Magazine never cost the Club a penny, as the revenue from the advertisers more than covered the only outgoings – the printer's bill and the cost of posting to something like 1,000 members.

No, my biggest problem was selling advertising and filling the equivalent number of pages with readable material. I'd lean on personal friends and Company customers to promote their business activities by taking space in our prestigious Club periodical, and/or provide some snippet of news or humour from which an interesting story might be fashioned by their old mate and honorary editor of the Magazine. After all, many of them were already members of the Eccentric Club.

We now go forward to the Spring of 1972, by which time three gaily coloured editions had been published. (Well, although I'd said they'd appear half-yearly it wasn't easy keeping to it, not with all that dearth of contributions). Then my old friend, Chris Henry, phoned one morning to suggest we meet for lunch at the Club.

Having decided how we wanted our steaks cooked, and sipping from a glass in the bar while waiting for the kitchen to get them right, he said, 'You're always crying, in that Magazine of yours, that not enough people are telling you stories – try this one on for size!' He pulled a press cutting out of his wallet.

Now those who know Chris Henry, and there are many, must be well aware that Christopher speaks in a far richer idiom than in the lines I've just given him. He is one of the most colourful Irishmen I've met – and I've met a few. A brief run-down on the man wouldn't come amiss here – especially as he also happens to be a most successful 'hunter' in his own right.

Chris was one of a family of 11 children in the village of Cloonlarnin, County Sligo, where – at the age of 16 – he ran his own one-man business of roof-thatching, lime-burning, and pig-slaughtering. His fee for slaughtering the pig was to retain its head (nobody had money on that poverty-stricken west coast in those days). Today, he is

Chairman of the multi-million pound Henry Group of Companies.

I first met him when he joined Crews Hill Golf Club in 1958, roughly about the same time as I did. He and his wife, Mary, joined me and mine – together with six other pals and theirs – when we went on a coast-to-coast tour of the United States in 1970, based on an invitation to visit Nashville, Tennessee, from some of the leading citizens of that city. It was the subject matter of my first book, *Start-Off-Smashed!* which also happens to be the initial letters of what it's all about – Super Trans-Atlantic Reciprocal Trips Organised For Friends of Sam Morley and 'Skinny' Huggins – Eccentric Diplomats! It was published in 1973 but, as it's just possible that not everybody has a copy, I'll quote my description of Chris Henry from it.

> In 1946, at the age of 18, Chris Henry left the green mountains of County Sligo in order to dig holes in England for the firm of Murphy, civil engineering contractors. John Murphy having left Ireland a few years earlier to seek his fortune in a similar way. It didn't take Chris very long before he decided to buy his own pick and shovel, and dig for himself instead of for Murphy. Since then, he has steadily built a substantial muck-shifting, demolition, groundworks, and general building business based in a newly-built office block in the St Pancras area.
>
> In those early days, however, he would supplement his earnings with the shovel by 'moonlighting' as a professional heavyweight boxer and a dance-hall 'bouncer'. But I don't believe he ever could have wanted to hurt anybody. He is a kindly man, whose granite-like features totally belie his warm and friendly disposition.

The book was published somewhere around April 1972, and it was about a month or so later that Chris was showing me that newspaper cutting at the Eccentric Club.

It was a photograph from the *Esher Times*, showing the wooden grandstand and ancillary buildings of Sandown

Park racecourse burning fiercely, with lots of firemen, pumps, and hoses in the foreground. The caption read, 'Sandown Up in Smoke' – and a reporter had spread himself over half a column on the subject.

When Chris had finished telling me the story-behind-the-story over that steak, there was a lot more 'meat-and-gravy' to it than there was in that half-column. Or, come to think of it, in that steak!

Before starting the Sandown saga, I should explain that it is not only the lead-in to another example of how to succeed in business without really trying – but also shows one or two aspects of tendering over and above some of the systems described in the earlier pages. Although well laced with laughter, there's a lesson there somewhere of how a 'broth-of-a-buccaneer' steps in where angels-fear-to-'trade' and gets himself a doubtful prize, demanding as it does a tight price and a tough finishing date – yet makes good to everybody's surprise with a far bigger 'bag of booty' through having spotted a short cut that wasn't on the map.

It all comes clear as the story unfolds, using the actual names of the principals, and introducing them in the order that P.A.G.'s team were brought 'on stage'.

Client is United Racecourses Ltd – the owners of Sandown Park Racecourse, where I've spent many happy – although sometimes not too lucrative – hours speculating on which 'critter' would lead the field up to the post on that grand and scenic circuit. With the help of tens of thousands of fans like me, their coffers no doubt bulged in much the same way as P.A.G.'s did. So they decided to build the grandest of grandstands, whereby at least three times the people who initially went racing there could enjoy the sport amidst luxury and facilities never before experienced.

Architect is Fitzroy Robinson & Partners, one of the most prestigious practices in the country, with no shortage of handsome structures to their credit both home and abroad. (I know all that only too well now, but I don't think I'd ever heard of them at the time it was all taking place. Not their fault – I just wasn't in their league!)

Client's instructions were no doubt highly complex. But somewhere among them was possibly a clear-cut request to design something that would make the Ascot folk spittin' mad when they saw the little touches they wish they'd included, when they did their's about ten years earlier. Like a huge panoramic and elegant restaurant from which you can watch live racing while lunching or taking tea in style – instead of being incarcerated out of sight of everything at the back of the stands.

In view of its complex nature and the needs to get a commitment on starting and finishing dates, it was decided not to waste a lot of preliminary time in preparing all the 'bumph' that accompanies an open-tender project. Instead one firm would be chosen and a limited brief prepared. It would be a negotiated contract, subject to stringent conditions and penalties. Much the same as was done with Laing's when the re-building of Ascot's grandstand was negotiated.

Main contractor is Trollope & Colls Ltd, a member of the Trafalgar House Group and long established in the City of London. They undertook to start and finish the job within 12 months. Whereupon Client arranged with the racing authorities for all their usual fixtures to take place elsewhere, and to return to their rightful venue exactly one year after the closing date.

But before any building work could start, it was necessary to knock down the old wooden grandstands – two of them, about 60 feet high – and a number of smaller outbuildings. They then had to be broken up, carted away, and the site left clean and level ready for a new set of foundations to be dug out and laid.

Main contractor offered the demolition sub-contract to two firms (without a doubt M.C. was 'hunted' by many others – but time was short) on the clear commitment that they would start on day one and be out and finished in nine weeks. The Henry Group put in the best figure and got the job.

Main contractor, no doubt under pressure from elsewhere, then said, 'Look, we find we can't wait nine weeks. We want you to put in more men and equipment so that you can get out in six weeks.' 'O.K.,' said Henry, 'I shall have to up my price by 50%.' It was agreed and the order amended accordingly.

When Tom Costello, Chris Henry's foreman and fellow-countryman from County Mayo, arrived on site with his trained band of 'wreckers', he took a walk round the doomed buildings, did a bit of thinking, and got on the phone to Chris at the office.

'Chris,' he said, 'burning this lot down is going to be a lot cheaper, quicker and cleaner than knocking it down.'

'Knowing your capability,' replied Chris cheerfully, 'you must be right!' His opening phrase is his favourite one. No matter what you're talking about, he'll use it half-a-dozen times in a normal conversation.

So Tom got the boys to pour two dozen 40-gallon drums of diesel oil over the lot, and, with a 5-gallon jerrican, laid a trail of petrol from the centre of the oil-soaked stands to a suitable vantage point about 75 yards away. He looked round and had a count up, to ensure none of the boys were still in the danger area, lit a fag, took a deep draw, and applied the still-burning match to the end of the petrol 'fuse'.

Down that trail swept the flame, faster than any four-footer had ever galloped up the final half-furlong on the track nearby. Then, with a 'Whoosh!!' and a roar, the stands turned into a 'Fourth-of-July' conflagration that lit up half the county!

It wasn't very long before the Fire Brigade and news-hounds were there in full force. The Fire Chief was quoted in the *Esher Times* the following morning:

'There was no danger to people or property outside the racecourse and it was a good exercise for my boys. I don't believe we've seen one as big as that since the London Blitz.'

'We'd have had it under control a lot earlier,' he went on, 'but as fast as we'd subdue the flames at one end of the buildings there'd be this crowd of mad Irishmen dashing about pouring more oil wherever they thought the fire wasn't burning fast enough!'

Well, that's the gist of the story Chris told me over lunch a few weeks after the event. I wrote it up for publication in the Autumn issue of the Magazine, under the heading, 'Hot Tip At Sandown!', with a copy of the newspaper photograph and caption. My final paragraph from the Magazine read:

'Sandown is due to re-open for racing at the beginning of August next year, with new stands and public amenities superior to anything else in Europe.

If and when they do, it can be claimed that the builders were able to meet their tight programme thanks largely to an Eccentric Irishman and his equally eccentric staff!'

Once Chris received his copy he asked if he could have another 30 to pass around among his friends.

Now, so far in this chapter I've used about 2,500 words to set a scene in which my own business interests play no part, direct or indirect. In tackling the magazine project I was pandering to the ego of a would-be creative writer. The Sandown story was one of many produced – some created by me, others edited from members' offerings – to fill available space. There were tales of golf, boats, travel, art, bridge, theatre – to name but a few. The fact that this one is about construction, with which my business was involved, is coincidental. After all, my kind of product was marketed through electrical consultants to electrical contractors, hardly ever by direct association with big builders or architects.

Sandown Park I knew well because, as already stated, I've often gone racing there. Fitzroy Robinson & Partners I did not know because, as already stated, I rarely got

"We'll just have one more for the road, Patrick!"

involved with architects – only engineers. Trollope & Colls I knew, as a name to be seen on building-site boards around London ever since I can remember. Some of our stuff may have gone into some of their projects – but as our orders would have come from electrical, not main, contractors, I don't recall any involvement with them prior to 1972.

It all changed quickly after that magazine article!

A few weeks after sending Chris those 30 copies of the *Eccentric Magazine*, I received a letter from Fitzroy Robinson & Partners (Right – now I can no longer claim not to have heard of them). It was typed on heavily embossed paper and signed by one of the partners – Geoffrey Rainbird. He opened the batting by introducing himself as Architect for the new Sandown Grandstand complex, and explained how taken aback he was to see his merrily burning project featured on the 9 o'clock T.V. news on the night in question. He couldn't see much point in climbing out of his slippers and armchair to hot-foot it over to Esher that evening, but wasted little time in arriving on site bright and early the next morning. To quote from his letter:

I was greeted by the burly Tom Costello; who quietly walked by my side as I took in the scene. And what a scene! Where the equivalent of a giant football grand-stand had stood unscathed only 24 hours earlier, was now a vast open space. Nothing remained but heaps of white ash, a few twisted steel girders poking up drunkenly out of the ground, and some blackened timber beams with wisps of smoke still rising from their charred remains.

I thought of the tight target dates that had been set and the fact that the site would now be cleared for the contractors to make a start within four days. (Let alone the six weeks for which it had been agreed to pay Henry more money, because he'd been asked to estimate on the basis of it taking nine). I thought of the massive savings the Henry Group must have made in their labour and cartage estimated costs when pricing the job!

Turning to Tom, I observed, 'This seems a very convenient fire you've had here, Tom?'

Nodding his head, he replied, slowly and confidentially, in his soft Irish brogue, 'Ah, Mr Rainbird, there's more ways of killin' a pheasant than fahtin' in its ear!' . . .

I could read no further. My secretary came running in when she heard me explode, and stared at the tears of laughter streaming down my face. Without a word I handed her the magic letter and watched her through water-filled eyes as she ploughed through the opening paragraphs. Her screech brought the sales manager in a-running from his adjacent office, and we had to wait while he read what was disrupting the place. I remember my secretary wondering whether that might be the way they hunted for pheasant on the west coast of Ireland!

Once strong enough to face whatever else Mr Rainbird had to offer, I waited till the still giggling pair had left the room, and went on reading.

Following that excerpt from his unofficial 'minutes' of the site-meeting with Tom Costello, he told me he'd always been suspicious of how that convenient fire started, and on reading the story, rang Christopher up to tell him as much. Also to congratulate him on having had it recorded in such a masterly fashion!

He now wrote to say how much he had enjoyed reading the rest of the Magazine, too. Chris had told him that I had written a book recently, about a golfing trip across the United States and in which Henry was featured more than somewhat. Chris had also explained that I did all my writing for fun, but that the serious and breadwinning side of me was committed to making commercial lighting fittings.

'Well', wrote Mr Rainbird as he neared the end of his unique two-page letter, 'I like your style of writing.

Would it be possible for me to buy a copy of your book, and if there happens to be any literature on your lighting fittings would I find it as entertaining as I did your Magazine?'

'What a lovely man!' I thought, as I personalised a copy of *Start Off Smashed!* with a suitable inscription on the opening page. It was then enclosed with a marketing pack of literature for delivery by hand when the van was in the W.1 area later that day. Also enclosed was a long letter of appreciation for all he'd written to me.

A few days later came a telephone call and an invitation to join him for lunch. When we met, it didn't take him long to finish with the pleasantries about the Sandown story and my book, and get down to whether my products were the sort of thing he might want to use on his projects.

He had two large developments in the design stage at the moment, both of which needed special treatment as far as lighting was concerned. There were over 6,000 lighting units involved and the firm he planned to have make them hadn't shaped up too well on another job recently. Was it within my capacity to do a prototype, achieve the high standard required, meet the tight delivery programme, and negotiate the budgeted price?

My answer to all his questions being a firm 'Yes!', a few days later I was invited to a meeting with the builder and electrical sub-contractors. Once all the preliminaries were resolved, they acted on an Architect's Instruction to place with us the first six-figure order my Company had ever received. And all six figures were to the left of the decimal point!

We achieved all that was expected of us without dropping any major clangers, with the result that, besides retaining the new-found goodwill of Architect, the main contractor thought well of us too. Not to mention the electrical sub-contractor, who was responsible for taking delivery and fixing our light fittings as they came to site. Over the ensuing ten years, we continued to get business and helpful introductions from both those sources.

With regard to Fitzroy Robinson & Partners, I don't remember how many times over the same period they specified my old firm for their developments in London and the Middle East. One was the Abu Dhabi Exhibition Centre and Saluting Grandstand. It stands, tall, white and proud, on a sweeping arc of the Grand Cornische motorway bordering the sky-blue Persian Gulf (flanked by other Fitzroy Robinson developments with my lights in them). Its design, especially the soaring cantilevered canopy, would make a racegoer think he was back at Sandown Park. Only instead of a green ribbon of turf in front of it, there's a wide dual carriageway along which loyal Abu Dhabians can march and salute their ruler – on such occasions considered important enough to halt the endless roar of vehicles hurtling past in both directions.

Although it's nearly four years since I retired and went in for writing instead of lighting, Geoff Rainbird and I are still good friends and meet up for an occasional lunch and chat about golf handicaps and old times. He's now senior partner of his practice. I sent him a rough draft of this to ask if he had any objection to it from a professional or personal point of view. 'Marvellous!', was all he said. He re-enters the book in Chapter Fifteen, and once again made no bones about his approval when sent a draft of the chapter.

There ends another example of how friends, clubs and hobbies outside of the 'hunt' for business, can bring unexpected rewards. Rewards often far greater than those to be won by charging around with a mob of other 'hunters', each with beady eyes glued on the same elusive quarry!

And talking of rewards – remember that slap-up dinner for four promised by Sir Malcolm Miller to he who would found an Eccentric Magazine? – it never did materialise!

There endeth the second lesson!

——— 9 ———

Putting-on-the-Ritz!

Ross McWhirter was a gifted man of letters. With his twin brother, Norris, he originated the *Guinness Book of Records* in 1955; a fascinating work of reference updated each year and, until 1986, still compiled and edited by Norris.

Ross lived in Enfield, where he was murdered in cold blood by the I.R.A. on the front steps of his home, back in 1975. To help cope with her grief after witnessing the tragedy, his wife, Rosemary – who had always worked hard for worthy causes in and around Enfield – threw herself with renewed energy into fund-raising and visiting the less fortunate in the surrounding homes, hostels and hospitals.

Group Captain Leonard Cheshire, V.C., D.S.O., D.F.C., was a personal friend of Ross McWhirter, and Rosemary had played a large part in raising support from local commerce and industry for a Cheshire Home to be built in Enfield. It was opened in January, 1976.

Persuading even the most generous of folk to part with charity money, for even the worthiest of causes, is a thankless and uphill slog. There are so many causes and they all need so much. But before I get on to the 'nitty-gritty' of this third and last 'hunting' story, a word or two about the origin and purpose of the Cheshire Homes wouldn't come amiss here. Who knows, it might encourage one or two readers to bear them in mind when planning their schedule of annual donations to favourite charities. Responsible individuals and business houses should set aside at least 5% of personal income or trading profits for those in need. Among these I do not include the Inland Revenue or your High Street betting shop!

Group Captain Cheshire was one of our foremost bomber pilots in World War II. He was also the official British observer when the second atomic bomb was dropped on Nagasaki in 1945. On retirement from the R.A.F. he sought a means of relieving human suffering to make amends for the years so many of us spent in creating it.

In May 1948, when about to dispose of Le Court, a large but somewhat neglected house he owned in Hampshire, he was told of an old man dying of cancer in hospital, without friends or a place to go to. Leonard Cheshire took him home and nursed him until he died. He found more lonely people who, rather than spend the rest of their days in geriatric wards, were quite ready to accept the make-shift arrangements at Le Court as a place they could call 'home'. Over the next few years the house was converted slowly into a modern building with equipment suited to its new purpose.

Today there are over 70 such homes in the United Kingdom, and about 100 others in various parts of the world. They are for young or old, of any denomination, and from every walk of society.

The Cheshire Foundation Homes for the Sick is a registered charity and owns all the properties. It acts as a guarantor to the public that the individual Homes bearing its name are run correctly. Each is managed by a Committee of unpaid volunteers drawn from the local community. Day-to-day administration is in the hands of a matron or warden over a small permanent staff.

The aim of the Homes is to give residents the greatest possible freedom to live normal lives, within the limits of their disabilities.

The disabled residents of any Cheshire Home come from its own immediate locality, where it is discovered all too quickly that genuine needs for further accommodation are always greater than its availability. And the entire cost of creating extensions has to be found from voluntary contributions – like donations, covenants, and legacies.

Rosemary McWhirter was on the voluntary Committee of Enfield's newly-completed Cheshire Home, and for which accommodation for a further ten residents was now urgently needed. She was also a 15-handicap member of Crews Hill Golf Club.

At the Club's annual Christmas lunch she found herself seated next to the Captain-elect, due to come into office at the A.G.M. – scheduled for the first Saturday in 1976. She used the opportunity well. Somewhere between the sherry and the port dawned a brilliant idea.

'What a marvellous thing it would be, Christopher, if Crews Hill Golf Club were to run a Charity Golf Day during your forthcoming year of office, with a view to raising funds toward building an extension at our new Cheshire Home!'

Now in case you haven't already guessed it, the Captain-elect happened to be that self-same gallant Irishman who featured so well in the previous chapter. Yes, it was none other but 'himself', Christopher Henry, who told Rosemary McWhirter that he thought the idea was a brilliant one. He would bring pressure to bear on the Club Committee and on all his friends in high places. By the time he'd finished it would be the biggest and best, star-spangled, festive and golfing hooley this side of the Macgillicuddy's Reeks! I think she half-believed him.

I wasn't at that Christmas lunch. In fact, due to playing my weekend golf on a Saturday, rather than getting involved in the over-crowded Sunday scene as of yore, I no longer took part in those weekly après-golf bar sessions with bosom chums like Henry. They were the days when I'd give my wife her Sunday morning cup of tea in bed before leaving the house at about 8am, and she'd call out, 'Lunch as usual, I suppose – 12.30 for 3.30!'

I'd seen the light several years before the period in question, with the result that the garden gets most of my Sunday mornings and I must say looks all the better for it. As does my Sunday lunch, now eaten freshly-cooked; instead of being fished from the depths of the oven – a dark-brown, coagulated mass welded on to a luke-warm plate – where it had spent the past two hours awaiting my unpredictable return!

Some time during March, Chris phoned and again asked me to meet him over a steak at the Eccentric Club. This time it was to tell me about the Crews Hill Christmas fest and his undertaking to Rosie McWhirter. It was the first I knew of it. He had now reached the stage where the Committee had agreed to close the course to members on Sunday, 25 September 1977 for the event to take place, and had put together a little *ad hoc* trio, consisting of himself, Rosemary, and one other, aimed at getting the show on the road. But time was marching on and he felt they were not making much progress.

The previous year the Eccentric Club had run its first Pro-Am. golf tournament. Only, as the owl has always been the emblem of the Eccentric, it was named a Pro-Owl. Jimmy Douglas, honorary secretary of the Eccentric Golfing Society, and I organised the whole thing, and learned quite a lot from some of the mistakes that were made. So much to be planned. Donations, celebrities, programmes, publicity, parking, catering, competitions, partners, crowd control, lunches, dinner, prize-giving, speakers, advertisers; to name but a few of the subjects that required detailed attention. My clerical staff at the office, not to mention their employer, were kept fully stretched on the organisation and correspondence involved during the five or six months leading up to the event.

Chris and I had played together at the event, which proved to be quite successful in raising a lot of money for whatever the Golf Society wanted it for at the time. I believe the Eccentric Club needed some expensive roof repairs and had asked the golfers to help find the cash.

Sitting round that lunch table in the Eccentric, Chris now spoke of the apparent ease with which the Pro-Owl seemed to run the previous Autumn, the difficulty he was having in getting his own show on the road, and the reason he was now buying me a steak and the better part of a bottle of Chambertin.

Opening with his standard, 'Knowing your capabilities, Sam,' he went on, 'you would be taking a great deal of worry off my mind if you would join my little organising Committee of Three.'

I thought of the hundreds of hours spent at home and in the office in putting the last one together, and knew there was going to be far more involved in this one. But when he again asked me to say yes to joining his little band at their next meeting on the following Monday evening, I wasted little time in agreeing to do so once he had named them. Despite the masochistic implications.

You see, at that time I knew Chris Henry very well – Rosemary McWhirter not quite as well, but the third member of their team not at all. Although his name was familiar we had never met. He was Victor Matthews, then the chief executive and vice-Chairman of the Trafalgar House Group and Chairman of the Express group of newspapers. He lived opposite Crews Hill Golf Club in his 500-acre farm and had joined the club a few years earlier when he first became interested in the game. Chris had asked his help in trying to drum-up some big name celebrities to appear and play on the big day.

Now that very first, and very large, City of London project to which I was appointed by Fitzroy Robinson & Partners, as described in the last chapter, was a Trafalgar House development. That is, the Trafalgar House Group was Client. Not with the intention of occupying the building themselves, but by putting up a quality office block on spec. and seeking a responsible business house to rent it when complete, although the lessee would often be given the option of deciding on internal fitting-out and finishes. Besides their many other interests – like the Ritz Hotel, Cunard, Cementation – the purchase of land and erection of speculative commercial buildings in the City of London was the principal activity of the parent Group.

There had been one or two other Trafalgar developments in which my firm became involved, by virtue of the goodwill built up in that first project, and currently I was 'hunting' for an extra large one. Its architect was unknown to me, but the builders were again Trollope & Colls – the wholly owned building subsidiary of Trafalgar.

To burn the midnight oil over the ensuing six months for a worthwhile cause, not to mention the countless telephone calls and letters from the office, would be more than justified if it helped me to get to know the boss of Trafalgar a little better. I looked forward to the following Monday's evening meeting in the lounge of the Royal Chase Hotel, Enfield, with considerable interest.

Unfortunately I was late. I'd spent almost the whole day on abortive meetings with the electrical contractors and consulting engineer for the Trafalgar development I was after, trying all I knew to persuade them to negotiate the design and order for its special lighting fittings with my Company. They in turn seemed to prefer placing it with one of my competitors and I arrived at the Royal Chase (aptly named in the circumstances) about 20 minutes overdue and somewhat jaded.

Chris took care of the introductions and, after my apologies for keeping them waiting (although it later transpired that Vic Matthews had only just beaten me to it) we got down to the business in hand.

It is not my intention here to describe the work involved in organising and running a Celebrity Golf Day – that could easily be the subject of a full-length book in itself – except that six months later it turned out to be quite a success and raised about £20,000 for the Enfield Cheshire Home.

At the end of that first meeting Rosemary said farewell and departed for some church-choir practice, while Chris, Victor and I sat in the bar chatting over a drink. Once away from the subject of the forthcoming event the conversation turned to more general matters.

'What's your line of country, Sam?' asked Victor politely.

While telling him that I made commercial light fittings, dear old Chris piped up with – 'Didn't you know? Sam's firm supplied all the lighting in your Billiter Street development.' (That was the six-figure job that followed up from my Sandown story. Chris knew all about it because he too had won some of the action on that one.) 'Did you really?' asked Victor. 'Are you doing anything for us now?'

I explained that I would like to have said yes, but it now looked most unlikely as, judging from reactions of those on whom I'd worked all that afternoon, the cards seemed stacked against us. He asked the name of the job and when I said 'Wine Office Court', he knew it instantly. 'That's a big one – even bigger than Billiter Street. Are you sure you could handle it if you got it?', was his next remark. The answer was a simple yes. He then asked if I'd done any other work for Trafalgar. I gave him the names of another one done for Trollope, and two for Cementation – a hotel complex in Panama and another at the Lot International Airport, Warsaw.

He noted all the relevant details in his diary and said he would check out the following morning to see how we'd performed on those jobs. If the answers proved satisfactory he'd find out what was happening on the one in which I was now interested. Providing an order had not yet been placed he could probably arrange for it to come to me, subject to my being prepared to match the lowest price tendered. His final words were to ring him at his office on his private line about noon the following day, I went home feeling a lot less jaded than when I arrived.

When I phoned he said that he'd asked around and nobody had anything too unpleasant to say about me or my Company. As a result he had spoken to Architect for the new project, and if all went according to plan I should hear from Architect or his electrical consultant within the next few hours. If I hadn't by 4.30 that afternoon I was to ring him again.

I thereupon cancelled a lunch appointment and had a sandwich sent up from the canteen.

Sure enough, the consultant's electrical engineer, a most amiable chap, came on the phone a couple of hours later to arrange a meeting for later that day. He had to come up by train from his office in Hastings, but as his home was in London it was something he did every day.

About ten years earlier my firm had supplied a lot of lighting and trunking for the new London Weekend Television building on the South Bank, and, during its construction we became very good friends with its admin. chiefs. A close personal friendship that's strengthened over the years. They've always encouraged us to make use of their excellent hospitality facilities if we needed to entertain in the area.

As we had not met before I told the man from Hastings to get a cab from Waterloo to the L.W.T. building, only a few hundred yards from the station, and that I'd be the slightly chubby, balding guy in the grey suit at the far end of the bar on the second floor. He said he too, was wearing a grey suit, but was neither chubby nor balding, and that his unruly curly grey locks brushed the gilded rims of his bi-focal spectacles. From which it can be assumed we had no difficulty in recognising each other when he arrived – especially as there were only three other people in the bar at the time!

His briefcase was full of drawings and papers, and he wasted little time in covering the table with them once we'd sat in a corner with our drinks. The appointment of a manufacturer to make these highly sophisticated air-handling luminaires was already well overdue. There had been problems on 'Olympus' over design and any further delays now would retard the whole project. Architect had given him his instructions that morning – providing he was satisfied my firm could meet the technical require-ments and would deliver on time, he was to negotiate with me on the basis of the figure they already had in for the job.

He explained that if it hadn't been for that instruction, the order would have been placed elsewhere within the next 24 hours; to a firm that had been recommended by others but in whose quality and delivery promises he himself had little confidence.

I felt myself warming to him. Especially when he said that, although we'd never met personally, he knew me and my Company quite well, and that, as he'd often come across our equipment on jobs where he'd served as an 'Olympian', he'd already told Architect that our reputation was sound.

As the job couldn't wait a couple of weeks while we did a full costing exercise involving all the unusual features of this unit, would I accept his word that a figure of £230,000 should prove itself adequate for me and acceptable to them? I said I would. 'Then,' he advised, 'deliver your quotation by hand to the electrical contractor tomorrow, setting out the quantities as shown in these documents and putting that figure on the bottom line. Phone it through first,' he went on, 'and tell whoever you send with it to wait for the order.'

As that order was bound to be subject to approval of a prototype we had to get cracking on making one immediately. The other firm had said they'd want 28 days for that, so I said we'd get it out in ten if we had to work through the night. And we did – got it out in ten with a couple of the lads working right through the ninth night. Having been given the opportunity, thanks to Victor Matthews pulling the strings behind the scene, it was most important that we went on to win some medals by our own efforts. To use an analogy:

As a mid-term new entry, and the son of an old friend of the headmaster, your classmates can be told to let you join in their games when you enter a new school. Well, they may have had to let you in, but you'll be expected to prove yourself by your own merits before anybody goes out of their way to keep you in. And it's not just the kids in the playground, but the prefects and teachers too, who don't take kindly to a new boy with links of friendship that go over their heads.

Fortunately we did acquit ourselves honourably, and a good rapport developed with 'Olympians', main contractor, and the sub-contractors who had to take delivery and fix our products. As a result, further business developed through them, and many are still friends with whom I enjoy a glass or a lunch today, without anybody trying to buy or sell anything.

After that first meeting in 1976, I sought Victor's help three more times in the ensuing six years, and twice was successful in negotiating substantial orders thanks to that help. The third, and biggest one, however, got away. Goes to prove you can't win 'em all!

My wife and I were among his personal guests at the annual all-Trafalgar Race Day at Sandown Park in June 1979. It was the third successive year he'd invited us, but 1979 was even more super-special than the two previous magnificent occasions. It was held on Saturday, 20 June and, as we downed a quick cup of tea and slice of toast before departing to Sandown, I looked through the runners and riders on the racing page while my wife ran her eye over the front of the morning paper. 'Never mind the horses', she suddenly burst out, 'look who's on the front page!' It was Victor Matthews, featured in H.M. the Queen's Birthday Honours List, as having been made a Life Peer!

Congratulations flew around thick and fast at glorious, sunny Sandown that afternoon. Although he had known about if for some time, nobody else seemed to have had an inkling – other perhaps than his wife, Joyce. He'd been asked to say nothing until the official announcement and had kept the secret well.

On reflection there must have been one or two privileged people taken into his confidence because, once the party was over at Sandown, he and Joyce invited 20 personal friends to be their guests for dinner in a penthouse suite at the newly refurbished Ritz Hotel. The souvenir menus with which we were each presented were embossed with the names of Lord and Lady Matthews, together with their coat-of-arms. Somebody had certainly moved fast there.

But then, as the Ritz now belonged to the Trafalgar House Group, of which Victor was managing director and vice-Chairman, its executive team must have enjoyed the reflected glory and the chance to show the boss they weren't as decadent as their building might have been at takeover.

He and I continued to be good friends, playing a 'cut-throat' round of golf most Saturday afternoons, until November 1985. Such times as he managed to win, which I think averaged out to a 50:50 ratio, he reckoned that taking that fiver off me gave far more satisfaction and pleasure than seeing his Fleet Holdings shares go up 10p during the week. And he had about two million of those!

He read the typescript of my last book. *In Search of Eastern Promise*, before it was published in October 1984, and kindly agreed to write the foreword. It was most complimentary.

In November, 1985, when United Newspapers made their successful bid for Fleet Holdings plc – which included the Express group of newspapers, he sold all his shares, bought at 22p five years earlier, for 375p – and immediately went to live in Jersey. It may have saved him £2½ million in Capital Gains Tax, but it left me without a partner for Saturday afternoons!

Telling human interest stories about Victor Matthews – other friendships made in the Trafalgar Group – the refurbished Ritz Hotel – and referring back to the continued pressure on contractors to complete to a deadline; I'll finish the third story in this trilogy on a light note, combining all four features.

Trafalgar bought the Ritz in 1976, and put in one of their building subsidiaries to perform what finished up as a £12 million refurbishment contract. The firm, Bridge

"I do enjoy these Saturday afternoons with you, Sam."

Walker Ltd, was once owned by Victor Matthews, who sold it to Trafalgar in 1967 before joining the parent Board. By the time the Ritz job came along he was too busy with far bigger things than to watch the day-to-day performance of his old team.

But day-to-day progress at the Ritz, just across the road to, and visible from, Victor's office in Trafalgar's H.Q. at 1 Berkeley Street, was not to his liking. The Ritz was his 'baby' and he felt vulnerable. So he pulled out his old firm, and put in Trollope & Colls to get things speeded up to the high standard he demanded. The Trollope & Colls director in charge, John Robinson, was put under strong pressure to meet a deadline for completion by September 1978.

John also happened to have been the project director in charge of the Wine Office Court job described earlier in this chapter. The one Victor Matthews helped me to get after that first meeting to discuss the Cheshire Homes Celebrity Golf Day. John and I became good friends and have remained so ever since. We meet a lot and we laugh a lot.

Two months before the Ritz deadline John joined me for some lunch at the Eccentric Club. Trafalgar were screwing him into the ground for completion and he needed some 'fresh air'. He spent most of the meal weeping and wailing into his glass. He needed 20 top-quality painters to get the job finished on target and just couldn't find them. That is, not up to the standard he needed for the Ritz.

A telex was sent to his office when I got back to mine. This was it:

JOHN ROBINSON ESQ, TROLLOPE AND COLLS LTD
25 CHRISTOPHER ST. EC1

UNDERSTAND YOU URGENTLY NEED 20 TOP-CLASS
PAINTERS FOR YOUR RITZ PROJECT. MAY WE OFFER
OUR SERVICES.   SIGNED:
JOSH REYNOLDS   MIKE ANGELO

'FUZZ' CONSTABLE	JOHNNY MATISSE
BERT GAINSBOROUGH	'TOOTHLOOSE' LE TRACK
WUNLUGH VAN GOCH	'PENNY' WHISTLER
FRANKIE HALS	WAREYA GAUGUIN
'OPEN' CEZANNE	HYMIE RUBENS
ROBBIE RENOIR	TONY CANELETTO
LENNIE DEVINCI	GIVUS DE MONET
'BOTTI' CHELLY	ADOLF HITLER
ALFIE MUNNINGS	SILVERDOOR DALI

It says much for the man that he didn't use one of them but still met the deadline!

Another memorable project in which I became involved through Victor Matthews and Trafalgar was the National Spinal Injuries Centre at Stoke Mandeville. Chapter Sixteen tells its story in detail.

The warmth and rapport with Trafalgar continues, and a great deal of the factual and technical information needed for these pages has come from good friends among its senior personnel. Researching with friends is done in much the same way as talking business with them – standing against a bar, or sitting across a lunch table. Only far more enjoyable. There's no undercurrent of urgency to buy or sell – just the pleasure of reminiscing over memories covering the best part of a 100 years (that's between two of us!) in a still fascinating industry. And over the eight months its taken to write this, I must have averaged three such meetings a week.

There endeth the third lesson!

Part Three has taken most research, especially as its theme came by way of an afterthought. It wasn't until most of the remainder was written or in draft form that there first dawned a need to present the target of a 'Hunt', more clearly. Once started it became a long and fascinating subject.

PART THREE

Fiddler-on-the-Roof!

10

Not All Clients Can Read Music!

A construction project starts in the ground and works its way slowly up to the roof. This story was built the other way round. It sets out from the Client-throne on the roof, or peak of 'Olympus', on a slow-motion downhill slalom, describing the scenery and characters on the way to the bottom. It was not necessary to describe in detail all the hunters we passed coming up for, whatever their interest, the styles of hunting are pretty much the same. In fact it can be said that in most cases the only differential would be to which of the 'Olympians' they pay homage for the favours they seek.

A piling contractor will need the goodwill of the structural engineer; high-speed lift specialists will pay court to the electrical engineer; ceiling-tile manufacturers will try to convince Architect that their tile pattern and edge trims will enhance his building better than that of their rivals; heating and ventilation companies will woo the mechanical engineers; drainage, paving and asphalting firms will pursue the civil engineer for involvement in the roads, subterranean tunnels and car parking facilities around the site.

Each of the consultants could have up to a score of trades under his discipline, and each trade could have just as many suppliers seeking nomination from the consultant for its products. All of which has been said elsewhere in these pages.

In addition, there are many sub-contractors to be engaged by main contractor and be his responsibility only. In other words, he doesn't need Architect's permission before making up his mind on which specialist firm of carpenters, bricklayers, tilers, plasterers, scaffolders, or plant-hirers to use. As a rule, builders today don't employ the vast number of tradesmen they once did. Vote-catching, feather bedding policies of successive governments and restrictive trade union practices are partially responsible for that.

Traditionally, the Construction industry has always employed a large percentage of nomadic labour – taken on when needed for a specific project, and asked to move on when their bit was done and their skills no longer needed. It was the accepted pattern. Then the 'leftie' politicians and the trade union leaders said, 'You can't tell a carpenter you don't need him any more on one site when you've got another site where you're still hiring carpenters. You've got to fit him in there or we'll shut down both jobs on you!' Never mind you've been waiting your chance to get rid of him because he was a bad worker or a trouble-making Commie!

Back in the 1960s and 1970s there were more big building sites at a complete standstill, often for a year or more, because of labour sabotage, than were working normally.

These days, building firms consist mainly of administrative and technical personnel with all the modern know-how at their fingertips, selecting the labour they need on a construction site from a vast army of self-employed artisans. Yes, the bloke fronting a picket line on a 'black' site a dozen-or-more years ago, is now a budding mini-tycoon in his own right – 'hunting' away like a good 'un for a chance to quote main contractor for all his shuttering, plastering, or what-have-you needs on the P.A.G. building.

We can look on that as a secondary 'Hunt', occupied with winning favour with main contractor. Now for the tertiary version.

Once the building is nearing completion, the proposed tenant or occupier becomes known, and this leads to a further 'Hunt'. Servicing contractors who want a chance to keep the building and its fixtures and fittings, in a clean safe, and usable condition; window cleaners, security guards, carpet-, curtain- and blind-cleaning specialists, onyx polishers, canteen contractors, maintenance firms for lighting, lifts, emergency services, boilers; and many more.

Then there are all those people selling office furniture, linen hire, stationery, calculators and copiers. Never a day goes by without another pile of post and a sequence of personal and telephone calls from 'hunters' of every description.

An old friend of mine was responsible for the internal administration of a newly built 28-storey office block from the day construction started, when his firm occupied temporary premises next door, until he retired ten years after completion. He had a never-ending fund of colourful stories about the day-to-day approaches from a wide range of 'hunters', hawkers and hucksters. Not just the run-of-the-mill teapot, typewriter and towelling purveyors, but also would-be 'Olympians', anxious to sell their skills and availability to design further construction projects if needed. These included chartered architects, surveyors and engineers, each asking to be borne in mind should extensions or alterations be envisaged at some future date; or perhaps somebody was thinking about developing another site where their services could be used. Estate agents, claiming un-named clients anxious to pay handsome, but again un-named, sums to acquire your building; the same estate agents who could also fix you up with other premises in the vicinity, on reasonable terms, should you think of accommodating the said client. Merchant banks and moneylenders (what's the difference?) with kind offers of help, should you have cash-flow problems, and demanding little or no interest (providing you left your mother in their vault as security). Insurance companies with a made-to-measure scheme that will not only cover the building against being struck by Halley's Comet, but will put up an identical one for you the following day!

Then there are the specialist bankers, like the Bombay and Ballybunion Credit and Commerce Corporation, who claim fantastic skill in handling the money of highly sophisticated international trading companies such as yours. But you're discouraged by the fact that, although the body of the letter is impeccably reproduced on good-quality embossed paper, they've twice spelt your name and address wrongly and differently in the badly typed-in bits. You also learn when popping out for a packet of fags from the newly opened sweets-and-cigs shop in your ground floor complex, that the widow-lady who runs it had an identical circular from the same firm that morning!

So far in this book about 30,000 words have been used to describe the chase for business in Construction. 'Hunts', whether primary, secondary, tertiary or whatever (what comes after tertiary?) have been studied and analysed. Those successful hunters who have now reached P.A.G.'s 20-storey site will spend up to three years there. Another 60,000 words could be used to describe the day-to-day 'hilaria' of site activity. But as this is all about the charge toward – not the action on – the 'battlefield', that's 60,000 words I won't have to write.

Nevertheless there are quite a few more needed if I'm to complete the picture described in the foreword.

Although almost everybody concerned with the 'Hunt' has now been introduced, there is one symbolic character featured constantly throughout these pages, but never yet in the capacity of a 'hunter'. His target and method of hunting differs from that of the straight 'up-and-down' traders introduced so far, but he should be rated the greatest hunter of them all.

I refer to Client – he who sits on the very peak of 'Mount Olympus' – the 'Fiddler-on-the-Roof!'

Brewer's Dictionary of Phrase and Fable states, 'To work a fiddle . . . usually implies some dishonest or "smart work".'

No self-respecting and God-fearing Client would get

involved in anything of a questionable nature – let alone dishonest. But to earn for himself the tag of 'Client' on a prime site in the City of London, he would have had to be a 'smart worker'! A very smart one, bearing in mind the entrepreneurial jockeying that takes place between 'fiddlers' competing for what is often compared to a 'licence to print money'! So any reference to a 'fiddle' or a 'fiddler' in what follows throughout this book is meant as 'smart work' or a 'smart worker'. By using quotes it will be known that I do not refer to musicians.

In the opening pages Client is introduced under a number of alternative 'hats'. But with the exception of the Property Developer, a client-hat on remaining heads is only a passing decoration. Not that a Hotel Group, or a Bank, or even our very own P.A.G. is not a 'fiddler'. Let's take a look at what might happen at a Board meeting when a decision to build is reached. The reasons that set P.A.G. in search of their 20-storeys of onyx have already been given. Parallel needs or whims would set a Bank or Hotel a-'fiddling' on a similar exercise. But unless they already own the land, or a building standing on part of the area they want to build on, they will need outside help.

Let's assume the Board of P.A.G. agrees that their branch at 57 Thingummy Row, E.C.5 is on the ideal spot for the new H.Q. building. One of their number admits to building a glass-house extension to his potting shed, single-handed, back home in Amersham. After a quick check round the table in case there's somebody with even more first-hand knowledge of construction, he'll be voted to head the Client-team that will monitor the project. But he'll just wear a No. 2 Client-hat. Chairman will always have his No. 1 Client hat hanging behind the door for attending those big prestige meetings.

After the appointment, No. 2 talks to staff-architect on P.A.G.'s premises department. One who knows a lot more about construction than No. 2, but not enough to be entrusted with 20 storeys of onyx. The S.A. is told what the Board have in mind, and is then asked to do some calculations. Like, how big a plot of land will be needed for ten storeys capable of housing the staff and equipment the Board want to install there, plus ten floors for letting to others on a profit-rental basis. Having done the sums they go down to Thingummy Row for a quiet look around, taking care that nobody at the branch knows their real reason for calling. After a further set of calculations, staff architect reports that they'll need to acquire the two adjoining properties to demolish along with their own, in order to put up the sort of building they have in mind.

This is where Client will have to be an above-average amateur 'fiddler', if he plans to go any farther without some sort of professional help. It takes a lot of pianissimo solo 'fiddling' to pull off an acquisition deal of this size. 'Pianissimo' is the operative word, if Client doesn't want to be outplayed by an independent 'string orchestra', with each 'fiddler' trying to play at a faster tempo than Client—or the rest of the group! I'll try to simplify the analogy.

There is no shortage of predators in the property development game. Once Client's interest is suspected, a predatory wheeler-dealer might try to buy the two adjoining properties first, using short cuts unknown to Client, and then offer them back at a fat profit. Or else make the re-sale a condition for Client to give him the job of developing the site for Client. Or he may know a competitor of P.A.G.'s who will buy and let off the properties, once again at a good profit to the predator, just to stop P.A.G. from flaunting its image in that particular area. A predator may know somebody waiting to build on that site – or to incorporate it into a larger development. In this case P.A.G. will be asked if it now wants to sell its Thingummy Row branch, after seeing the properties needed for its own development snatched from under its nose, and a sad and chastened Board will probably end up doing just that before going in search of a professional 'fiddler' to set them up with a new H.Q. elsewhere.

Professional 'fiddlers' study the daily financial and

property pages of newspapers, with a large-scale map of Central London on the wall in front of them and a copy of *Kelly's Directory* on the desk. If a share movement or item of property news provokes interest, then the place is pinpointed on the map and the area studied. If the geography looks right for a development programme in the near or distant future – but not too distant – then *Kelly's* is studied to check the occupants of premises that might play a part in that development. If the occupants are tenants, or part of larger groups, the owners would be sought and sounded out whether they'd consider selling their freeholds. The approach would be smooth and innocent of any 'fiddling' overtones. Predator will probably imply he's acting for some un-named charity with modest funds to invest in a steady income from sound tenancies.

They also have a 'network of spies' staked out in places like Town Hall Planning Offices, Companies House, Land Registry, Stock Exchange, and most top estate agents, who are on the phone as soon as the introductory bars of a 'fiddle'-in-the-making are heard. Predator immediately starts tuning-up for a full-scale counter-'fiddle'!

To take on the formidable opposition as described, P.A.G. – our amateur 'fiddler' – can employ a property agent to act for him, and ask that his interest and identity be kept a secret. Which, of course, will be done – unless the agent or one of his staff is a professional 'fiddler's-mole'! Or else get his solicitor to do it all, with similar attempts to remain anonymous, and hope his identity can remain a secret until the documents are signed.

Assuming he's achieved all that, it can have taken Client a number of years to sew up all the deals that went with owning the two adjoining properties needed to make up the site for his new H.Q. building. He may have had to pay through the nose for one of them, to a professional 'fiddler' who managed to beat him to the 'draw', and found himself the reluctant owner of two clapped-out banana boats, wallowing round the coast of Africa – the sole liquid assets of a moribund shipping company whose head office was in the other adjoining building in Thingummy Row. On the advice of staff architect he is now ready to talk to the authorities about outline planning permission for the development.

When a rich 'fiddler', amateur or professional, asks the Town Hall for permission to develop a valuable site, the powers-that-be see themselves in the role of a latter-day Robin Hood.

The attitude is, 'Hello, here's a lot of money going to be spent on making rich 'fiddlers', and their friends, even richer. If they need our permission before they can spend it, they will have to spend a little more and pay us a fee for being so accommodating.'

That does not mean the Town Hall expect a couple of cabin trunks stuffed with used fivers as their pay-off for O.K-ing the deal. What it does mean is that Client will be asked to do something nice for the ordinary people living or working in the vicinity of the site.

He is told that, if he can afford to put up a 20-storey office block on that bit of land, he can afford to donate some of it to the community and provide – at his own expense – certain amenities needed by the community in that area; and to a specification that the local authority will provide. It could be old people's flats, a shopping mall, a swimming pool and squash courts, or a public car park. Although if we're talking about the heart of the City of London the first possibility is an unlikely one.

That's what's known as a Planning-gain deal, and is quite often a game of catch-as-catch-can. The local authority always begin by demanding too much, and Clients are never happy about giving away any part of what they've fought so long and hard to get. A lot of time is then taken up while the Town Hall decides on what to ask for, before setting the details down on paper. The Client-team then calculate what it's going to cost in (a) lost space and rents, (b) building costs, and (c) expense of maintaining access to the donated area.

Negotiations drag on until a grudging compromise is reached. It isn't as though Client, before he started 'fiddling' for the adjoining properties, could have asked Town Hall what they might ask in exchange for planning consent, if he were able to buy them. Predators have their 'undercover agents' planted in every planning office, and by the time Client's back at his own desk after that initial chat at the authority's H.Q., professional 'fiddlers', far and wide, will have been put on the alert.

That's the end of phase one. P.A.G. now owns a couple of scruffy old properties alongside their branch in Thingummy Row, and has agreed to build a planning gain of a public library, a sub-post office, and a Citizens Advice Bureau. It is now ready to start phase two – the design and construction of 20 onyx-clad storeys on that site without wasting any more time. Which takes us back to page 7 in this book, where the first paragraph explains P.A.G.'s decision to have a new H.Q. building and the second begins to tell how they went about it. Many frustrating years may have elapsed between those two consecutive paragraphs.

11

Jokers Wild!

It might appear that, having named a number of potential Client-types in the opening paragraphs of Chapter One, I've picked on the insurance business to make an object of ridicule. Well that's not true. This book is not out to ridicule anybody, although a little irreverence is sometimes useful for highlighting a point worth making. With the exception of the Property Developer, all the other Client headings referred to can easily be substituted for our dear old friends, the Prummercial Assurance Group.

Given the opportunity, any of them would bask in the pomp and circumstance that goes with the chance to wear that Client-hat at a jaunty angle, and would strongly deny that their shareholders and investors – or taxpayers – might have to pay more than otherwise if they did so. But, unless firmly led by a dictatorial despot who knows how to deal with pitfalls and obstacles, the project will be littered with indecision, wrong decision, and counter-decision by the board or committee responsible for it. Egotism and ignorance can turn an amateur Client into a God-given sucker, and many a predatorial 'hunter' will be waiting to take him for a ride!

That's why so many projects, especially those initiated by central or local government, start out as, say, £5 million jobs for completion in 12 months, and clock up something like £10 million and three years before showing any signs of completion.

Every pack of cards has a joker in it, and that title belongs to H.M. Government's Property Services Agency, as far as my pack of Clients is concerned. Over the years its title and responsibilities may have varied, but never its ability to squander public money. One or two stories to this effect are worth re-telling.

When my factory was in Thetford, Norfolk, I also ran a small electrical contracting unit from there. Royal Air Force and United States Air Force bases are scattered all over East Anglia, and much of the construction work carried out in those bases came under the control of what was then the Ministry of Public Buildings and Works (M.P.B.W.).

I don't remember which of the airfields it was, but we quoted the M.P.B.W. for electrical work on a new workshop and administration block to be erected there. Our tender was accepted and we got the order from the main contractor responsible for its construction.

Things went well until, approaching the end of the job, we were asked to put in more men and have people working weekends over the ensuing month or so, in order to get our contract completed before the scheduled finishing date. For which we were to be paid more money. Not only us, of course, but main contractor and all the other trades engaged on site.

It wasn't that war was imminent and that our project was meant to house a secret vital link in the country's defences, therefore needing to be fully operational without delay and regardless of expense. It was just that the powers-that-be had decided on a re-scheduled utilisation of buildings on the airfield, and the one we worked on was no longer wanted. A new one had been designed to suit a different need, and work would start on it just as soon as ours could be demolished and the site prepared for the replacement to go up.

But it wasn't as easy as that. The R.A.F. had ordered a new building from the M.P.B.W. who could not hand it over until the R.A.F. signed an acceptance saying it was all nicely finished and met their specification. And, not until it was their property, could the R.A.F. instruct the

M.P.B.W. to arrange for its new building to be knocked down and put up an even newer one in its place.

With the result that everybody working on the original project was paid unstinting acceleration money to complete their contract, down to the last specified detail, just to allow those waiting 'dozers to move in and start knocking it down!

For the next story on the same theme, I go back to one published in the same edition of the *Eccentric Magazine* as 'The Great Fire of Sandown'. This one I called, 'The Most Expensive Dog Kennel in Town!'

It concerns Euston Tower, a 37-storey speculative office block rising over the corner of Tottenham Court Road and Euston Road, and completed in 1968. With its modern, open-plan, air-conditioned offices and close proximity to stations and shops, the developers were confident there would be little difficulty in finding a tenant to lease the whole building from them.

But times were hard and it stood empty for two years.

Then along came Harold Wilson's Government, and said, 'That's just the kind of building we want. With its wide-open office floors at every level, instead of a crummy rabbit-warren of cubicles, it'll be the ideal head-quarters for our new Ministry of Technology.' The Property Services Agency promptly took out a term tenancy on the whole building at a yearly rent of £2 million.

Hardly was the ink dry on the agreement than Mr Wilson went to the country in the 1970 general election, and failed to make the grade. In came Edward Heath and his Merry Men, who wasted little time in killing the idea of a Ministry of Technology stone dead!

That left the Government paying £2 million a year for 37 very large floors of empty office space it didn't need. So they put in two Alsatian dogs and two Securicor men, who lived there in splendid isolation, with the complete run of the building, for the next 18 months.

In the meantime the Property Services Agency thought

they'd try the Client-hat on for size. Knowing that established Civil Service tradition did not take kindly to open-plan offices, they employed contractors to do something about it. After all, the degree of privacy, area of desk-top, square-footage and grade of carpet, plus the number of prongs on a hatstand, are the very yardsticks and foundations on which our Civil Service is built.

So they installed about five miles of double-skinned, floor-to-ceiling, acoustic partitioning, and had electricians and H. and V. fitters alter wiring circuits, switching, thermostats and ducting, to enable each floor to be split into lots of individual offices. Each office was to incorporate two, four, or six windows, dependent on the grade of Civil Servant who was to occupy them. Every Government department has its own system of space allocation and location for its personnel, and would instruct the P.S.A. accordingly. But the P.S.A. prepared the building as they saw fit to suit whatever possible occupants were favourites at the time. And all was done while it was empty. Except, of course, for the two Alsatians and the two Securicor men.

Eventually, the Department of Health and Social Security took the lower 17 floors, and the Post Office the next 13 floors above them. But before anybody could move in, a lot more money had to be spent in again re-vamping partitions, lighting, etc. Not that there was anything much at fault with what was done previously; just that in the D.H.S.S. and Post Office, seniority was judged by whether a Civil Servant had one, three, or five windows to his office – not two, four, or six!

Think how much the country might have saved if the building had been allowed to remain as a vertical exercise yard for two dogs!

Partitioning plays a big part in fitting out a speculative modern office building. An initial specification with no occupant in view, will call for an open-plan layout that can take as many formations of partitioning as possible –

thereby allowing a free choice of shapes and sizes of enclosed areas, with doors and windows as required, to suit a tenant-Client once one arrives on the scene. Another 'Hunt' then starts in pursuit of the fitting-out contract. If tenant-Client is well used to this sort of thing he won't negotiate fitting out with the original consultants and contractors – he'll bring in his own 'Olympians' with their own band of followers. They will proceed to spend his money like water changing much of what the developer's team envisaged!

The old *Evening Standard* building near Fleet Street was pulled down in 1981, and a high-tech speculative office built by Trafalgar at an approximate cost of £27 million (that included over a quarter-of-a-million for sophisticated Morley lighting). Tenant-Client came along, put in his own management-fee 'Olympian' team to run a fitting-out contract, and spent another £13 million (including something like one hundred grand on de-sophisticating the Morley lighting!).

The last two paragraphs introduce another story in this 'joke' department. (It's not much of a joke when you remember who pays!)

The clock goes back about 12 years and sets the scene in Carey Street, the final resting place for so many hopes and ambitions. But this time it's not Bankruptcy Chambers, but a new speculative office block called Cleland House. This was another case where the M.P.B.W. rented the building to house a newly formed Government department – The Prices and Incomes Board.

Cleland House is a five-sided building, with three equal sides looking out on the passing show at the back of the Law Courts, joined up by two unequal sides that help to enclose a secluded courtyard with a pretty fountain and fishpond. Although only 6 storeys high it covers a large area.

Whereas it may have been a newly formed department, the P.I.B. staff were not new to the protocol that goes with office layout. The M.P.B.W. were instructed to partition each floor with a walk-around corridor on the outer perimeter, and each office provided with sufficient window space for its occupant(s) to gaze out on to the fountain and fish, while deliberating on nationwide policies of prices and incomes.

But by the time the M.P.B.W. had the place ready to house them, in came another Government. It decided to dispense with a Prices and Incomes Board, and pass its proposed duties to a newly created Office of Fair Trading and Consumer Protection which they housed elsewhere. While in a creative mood, they dreamed up a new title for the old Ministry of Labour and called it the Manpower Services Commission (M.S.C.), with added responsibilities over the old set-up. As this called for more staff and accommodation, the so far unused Cleland House was handed over.

Before accepting it the M.S.C. wanted a few changes made. All partitioning had to come down and be re-erected to provide the incoming folk with a view of the busy street scene below; while the communal access corridor was to follow the inner perimeter in sight of the fountain and fish!

It was a top-priority job and the M.P.B.W. (soon itself, to be changed to the Property Services Agency) responded gallantly. The site was a hive of activity, when came a panic call from the man in charge there. It had been overlooked that wiring to switches, plugs, etc., needed to be concealed inside partitions as they were erected. No time was wasted in getting a firm of contractors to send a score of electricians to Cleland House, and do as instructed by the M.P.B.W. man in charge.

Only when they got there with their tools, plant and materials, were they told of a change of plan. In order to allow partitions to be changed around more easily in future, it had been decided that all wiring must be run on their surfaces, and nothing concealed. Which meant that those 20 electricians stood around on site for a week or so with nothing to do, until partitions in any given area were fully fixed and panelled. And as the firm had negotiated generous daywork rates for providing their men so promptly, it wasn't too bothered itself about the delay.

As the managing director of that firm of electricians said, 'I'm one of the few people who can boast of being sent into Carey Street, and to have come out showing a profit!'.

The final story in this chapter concerns the British Museum.

About 15 to 20 years ago, an order was placed by the M.P.B.W. for the installation of a more sophisticated alarm system to protect the irreplaceable exhibits. Fire, Smoke, Flooding, Burglary, Theft, and no doubt other hazards, were all guarded against throughout the building. Miles and miles of cables were run in multi-compartmented steel trunking in the basements, and taken to sensors, alarm calls, bells and signs on all floors. The nerve centre was a large and complex control panel, to be fixed in the position currently occupied by the smaller and simpler burglar alarm panel down in the bowels of the Museum.

With all wiring completed and all protective appliances connected to the new panel came the time for substitution. The old panel was unbolted from the walls and floor, and temporarily suspended from the ceiling with bits of rope and old cable. The new panel was firmly fixed in position and the whole system thoroughly tested out. Permission was then sought from the Chief Security Officer in the Museum to disconnect the vital supplies from the old panel and take them into the new one. It meant that, for an hour or two, there would not be an operational alarm system in the Museum.

The Security chief sought permission from his chief, who in turn sought it from his. It went right through the Board of Trustees until it reached the Chairman, and even he wouldn't take responsibility for authorising it either. There had been a spate of theft in the Museum around that time, and nobody was prepared to stick a neck out by agreeing to the place being without alarms for a couple of hours.

And there the matter rested for the next dozen years or more: the new sophisticated and comprehensive system completed but never connected up, the old one still in service with its control panel hanging off the ceiling on bits of old rope and electric cables, and the contractor fully paid up as though he'd completed the job, and told to go away and forget it. After writing this I checked with a friend who works in the British Museum – who checked with Security. All I could learn is that the hanging panel is no longer there!

In all fairness I should close this chapter by stating that the stories belong to yesterday – when I knew a bit more of the day-to-day scene. They tell me the P.S.A. runs a much tighter ship now, and a lot of the old muddlers replaced with energetic, high-efficiency, finance-conscious officials; who, in turn, are carefully monitored by even more e,h-e,f-c officials controlling the public purse. I do hope so, but I've a sneaking suspicion that those old, bad, bureaucratic habits don't die off so easily.

12

Home-and-Away Bankers!

The Hong Kong & Shanghai Banking Corporation gave their architect a simple brief:

> Please pull down our lovely old Headquarters-building on the corner of Queens Road, Hong Kong. Having stood there for nearly half a century, and been looked upon as one of the most pleasing examples of architecture of its period, it is now completely inadequate for our needs. In its place will you kindly build us the best bank in the world.

The new bank – 'ready in all its magnificence to thrill the resident and impress the visitor' – opened in October, 1935. It was years ahead of its time. A helicopter landing pad was sited on the roof, tubular steel scaffolding was imported from England, the building was entirely air-conditioned, and a new formula of high-tensile steel was used for the first time for the complete structure.

The comment at the beginning of the last paragraph was taken from the Hong Kong *Morning Post*, 17th October 1934; the day the Governor of the Colony laid the foundation stone to 'the Bank'. The newspaper article finished with – ' . . .Then we shall, in another 50 years perhaps, be greeting a greater skyscraper – for who can predict with certainty what Hong Kong's needs will be in 1984?'

Well, for a 50-year-old uncertain prediction that wasn't a bad guess. The new 600-foot high Hongkong Bank, as it now prefers to be called, started to function in July, 1985.

The opening paragraph of this chapter can be date-lined some time in 1929. It was 50 years later, early in 1979, when 'The Bank' decided on a 'replay', and commissioned a top international design team to carry out a feasability study, with a series of outline recommendations for a new 'best bank in the world'. The Head Offices built in 1934 were once again proving hopelessly inadequate for its needs.

The designers did their homework, and their comprehensive report formed a large part of the Hongkong Bank's brief when it invited seven of the world's leading architects, renowned for innovative design, to take part in a limited competition. They were given five months in which to submit their suggestions for as futuristic and impressive a building as the 1935 edition was considered to be when it opened on the same site. Two of the selected practices were British, two American, two Australian, and one from Hong Kong. Architectural Competitions are described in Appendix A.

Foster Associates of London, in conjunction with Ove Arup & Partners, Consulting Engineers, were declared the winner. It was a unique project involving complex engineering. In researching for this part of the book I marvelled at some of the problems and the ingenuity shown by the 'Olympians' in tackling them. Avoiding technicalities, here is a brief description of one feat that impressed me.

Shortage of fresh water being a chronic problem in Hong Kong, it was decided to bring in seawater from the harbour for air-conditioning and toilet-flushing systems. After all, 3,500 people were going to work in the place. It involved running three 30-inch diameter pipes – flow, return, and spare – in a 20-foot diameter tunnel. The tunnel was first driven vertically through massive granite to a depth of 130 feet below the basement of the building, which itself was 70 feet below street level. It then ran for a quarter of a mile to its maximum depth of 230 feet, before being brought to the surface to a pumping chamber by the side of the Star Ferry terminal. That particular spot was chosen deliberately, as the frenzied churning of paddles while ferries manoeuvred in and out every few minutes would help circulate the effluent around the rest of the South China Sea; thus preventing the build-up of a hot-spot that might well have parboiled surrounding marine life before it could be hooked or netted.

It was necessary to go that deep with the tunnel in order to avoid poking holes in the underground railway system; not to mention chopping into the forest of steel piling supporting high rise buildings that lay on its line.

Throughout its construction, the bewildering design of 'The Bank' has attracted lots of interest and criticism, and no doubt will continue to do so for the next 50 years. This book is not meant to be an assessment of modern architecture – there are enough pundits about without looking foolish by voicing my own untrained opinions – but I'll need to explain the reason for going a third of the way round the world to start this chapter.

Part Three relates to Clients as 'hunters'; 'fiddling' away to acquire sites for future developments in much sought-after areas like the City of London. Well, building land on Hong Kong Island is in far greater demand than in the City of London, and fantastic sums are paid for the privilege of knocking down one perfectly good building in order to replace it with a higher and more sophisticated one. Three or four times the letting areas, and corresponding rents, are thus obtained.

In the opening pages of Chapter One, Banks were referred to as an example of a potential Client; and Banks are what this chapter is to be about. But not any old bank. The intention is to compare Client performance in the building of new head offices for two of the most successful banks in the world in crowded city centres.

Both the 600-foot Hongkong Bank and the 610-foot National Westminster Tower, were completed in the first half of the 1980s within a couple of years of each other. Their almost identical heights, identical objectives as H.Q. buildings, and proximity of completion dates, justify using them, albeit cryptically, for the title of this chapter.

But other than those three factors they don't have much more in common.

The Hongkong Bank tore down its existing H.Q. building, put up a temporary one to continue trading, and moved into the new one – consisting of 0.8 million square feet of usable office space out of a gross area of 1.1 million – all within four years. The Nat West Tower took 22 years from concept to completion, finished with 0.29 million square feet of offices out of a gross area of 0.9 million, and irrevocably lost the use of its site for its H.Q.

And just to throw in a bit more interesting food for thought: New York's Empire State Building went up about 50 years earlier. At 1,250 feet to the observation-tower platform on the 102nd storey, it is roughly twice the height, and has twice the number of floors, as our two 'latter-day' bold and striking monuments. With 2,000,000 square feet of rentable office space, it was let and occupied within two years of the site being cleared for excavation to start. But then, it was built by entrepreneurial professional developers wearing the Client-hat – not bankers!

The Hongkong Bank was a Construction Management project, without an official 'starting-price'. (Those wishing to know more about the aspects of Management in Construction should read Appendix B.)

Once news of the proposed super-development started getting around, the world's leading builders – and quite a few from the lesser-league tables – started 'hunting' in the time-honoured fashion. After a lot of sifting and weeding the field was narrowed down to six joint-venture enterprises. That is, the international builder sets up a new business with a suitable local contractor who is familiar with the labour, conditions and statutory requirements of the area. The former uses his expertise in high technology, procurement, and off-site control of sub-assembly, while the latter monitors the on-site progress. This was especially necessary in Hong Kong, where the crowded and cramped conditions, together with lack of storage space, meant so much had to be prepared away from the island and phased to arrive as required.

After a series of briefings by the 'Olympians', involving much descriptive data of what was in mind, the six contenders were given just seven weeks to prepare a 'thesis' on how they intended to go about it if they got the job. And, of course, what would be their charge for preliminaries, and what percentage of the total cost would be their fee.

The term 'preliminaries' for a project of this size is a bit of a misnomer. It means servicing the job throughout its duration, and providing all its needs, other than materials and labour, for its actual construction. Like supervisory and secretarial staff, together with site accommodation for 'Olympians' and sub-contractors; arranging enclosure of site, including security, safety and first-aid; temporary supplies of electricity, water, gas and telephones; scaffolding, cranes, plant, hoists, contractors lifts, gantries, walkways; insurance; rates on temporary buildings: toilet and canteen facilities; rubbish chutes and disposal. These are but some of the items that come under the heading of prelims.

The joint venture of John Lok–Wimpey Limited put in a 1,200 page 'thesis' to win the appointment. The figure I heard mentioned in Hong Kong for prelims and plant, including six tower cranes at about £1 million each, was something in excess of £50 million. When Wimpey were burning the midnight oil down in Hammersmith, during the seven weeks they were given in which to prepare their proposals, they split the project into about 100 separate 'work packages' – the first of which could start almost immediately if they were appointed. While the job was in progress, their own estimating team did an in-house exercise on what the eventual cost of the project might turn out to be. They came back with a figure of between £400 and £500 million. Not bad when you consider that the published final cost is given at about 10% over the top end of that estimate; and bearing in mind there must have been an awful lot that wasn't yet known when they did that exercise.

But amateur Clients will try to 'fiddle' at Construction and thereby put unnecessary extra strain on a carefully planned project. Once a work-package is designed, put out to tender, and let to the winning 'hunter', any re-decisions by Client will not only cause cost-loaded delays, but open the door for a tight-priced sub-contractor to make that killing he needed to get his job out of the 'red'.

Bankers are graded pretty much the same as Civil Servants, and it is not unknown for senior grades to pull rank by countermanding decisions made by their juniors, usually those only just their junior, and for what appears to be no better reason than a personal whim. Not that I'm suggesting anything like that took place during the building of the Hongkong Bank, but I do say it was not exactly unknown on bank-building projects, with which my own firm was involved.

However, when the Hong Kong job was about one-third of the way through, I understood there was quite a bit of acrimony flying around among the 'Olympians'. With the result that a world-renowned firm of consulting engineers were called in by 'The Bank' to do an in-depth independent survey of what was going wrong.

They spent about three months assessing the causes and remedies to the site problems. Whether they found Client responsible for creating most of the 'hiccups' is of no importance now. But, as a result of their recommen-dations towards a solution, an independent project-management consultancy was engaged, with the title of Project Co-ordinator, to stand in and act for Client in his dealings with the 'Olympian' team.

Before he set up his consultancy, Ron Mead was employed as Chief Engineer for the construction of the billion-pound Mass Transit Railway system of Hong Kong. I described some of it in my last book, *In Search of Eastern Promise* – as I did Ron and Glenys Mead. My wife and I enjoyed their company on more than one occasion when we first met in Hong Kong back in 1978. To achieve what the M.T.R. did under the streets of Hong Kong Island and Kowloon – including the laying of a pre-cast concrete twin railway tunnel on the bed of the ocean linking the two – and still finish on target after four nightmare years of disrupting the Colony, the Bank project must have looked like a game of Lego to Ron!

I believe his presence helped not only to keep the bankers off site, but also to ensure that decisions would be executed without change once they had been agreed. Where such changes were deemed to be essential, he interpreted them into authoritative technical presentations whereby the 'Olympians' could act with minimal delay and cost.

I'm given to understand that this created a great improvement to site progress and harmony, although it appears that Architect was a law unto himself – insisting on the last autonomous word wherever he thought his authority might be at risk. But isn't that 'par for the course' with most architects?

In building their unique monument, Architect and 'The Bank' are to be congratulated for what can only be compared to the pioneering enterprise shown in the development of Concorde. The Bank is a bold venture into the future, and as such, like Concorde, its development incurred a great deal more capital and comment than a more conventional exercise might have done. But the end product is as far removed from a run-of-the-mill high-rise building, as the Anglo–French Concorde is from a Boeing 747.

It's the first multi-storey office block I've known where Architect has produced detailed colour-coded drawings for each floor, showing the layout, nature, and job identification of every desk, chair, filing cabinet, and any other piece of office furniture, plus decor, furnishings, and design of uniform clothing for staff using each area.

Waiting for lifts is always a source of irritation in tall

buildings, often due to their continued use by those employed in the place travelling on short runs between floors. In the Bank, escalators run continually between every level during normal office hours, leaving the 23 passenger lifts free for uninterrupted long hauls between stations spaced about eight floors apart.

The vastness of the main banking hall on level 3 is reached by escalator, from a sealed-air enclosure at street level. Members of the public depositing or demanding money or documents at one of the 44 black-marble electronic service tills, are treated to breathtaking views across the harbour, with the mountains of China in the distance. Though how many of those 44 tills will have a 'No-Service' sign in position on any given day is another matter; but it does mean there's always those panoramic mountains to gaze at while on a queue to a manned till, instead of just the dandruff on the shoulder of the person in front at your run-of-the-mill domestic High Street branch!

A composite handbook on how to use the mind-boggling building was prepared for distribution to all the staff, and training sessions ran for almost a year before the Bank became fully operational.

This one building will go on attracting more attention in the years to come than all the other Hong Kong high-rise developments put together. And there's no shortage of those. While drafting this chapter my wife called me to to come and watch a 'Tomorrow's World' T.V. programme, featuring the new Hongkong Bank. I gave her my draft to read when it was over, and was flattered when she said it was much easier to follow than the programme commentary. Not that there was anything wrong with the commentary, except it was done by a Chinese girl and we both had difficulty following her sing-song spiel. But I've noticed this for some time now – as the years roll along everybody talks more quietly and indistinctly!

'The Honkers and Shankers' (as 'the Bank' was affectionately known by afficionados), is a masterpiece of fruit-ful and futuristic design. Conceived and completed within four years by a team of highly skilled professionals, it had one objective from the start. All involved knew the part they were expected to play and, except for minor 'hiccups', it came off in all its glory as planned.

The National Westminster 'Tower of Babble', is the outcome of an inherited sequence of confusion and frus-tration stretching over 22 years. Internal impotence plus external politics gave a nil-return after an initial ten-year 'mating-season'. It was not until a banking 'marriage' was planned, with the 'groom's family' probably insisting that the 'bride's family' engage specialists before the ceremony could take place, that the first signs of fertility began to show themselves. Then came a 12-year 'gestation' period, culminating in a bonny, bouncing 610-foot 'baby', weigh-ing 128,000 tons!

What went wrong? Well, piecing the story together as given to me from a number of reliable sources, I'd say the 'battle' was a far bigger and more professional an engage-ment than could be handled by the 'Dad's Army' of enthusiasts who took it on back in the 1950s.

The National Provincial Bank was one of the original five clearing banks, with a branch in almost every High Street throughout the country. Its Head Office was a four-storey office block at No. 15 Bishopsgate, fronted by a majestic and spacious banking hall. Built in the 1860s as a triumph of modern architecture, 90 years or so later it had become scruffy, inefficient, and overcrowded. The bank decided that the time had come to rebuild its image with a spectacular landmark.

Surrounding buildings were steadily acquired until 1959, when they bought Gresham House, right next door to No.15 – and thereby completed a two-acre site of outright ownership. The City of London Club, a seedy and badly dilapidated building, adjoined the site. It agreed to the bank including its premises in the re-development programme, on the understanding it would be provided with new quarters within the overall plan.

So far so good. That's a lot farther than many amateur Clients might have got with a proposed City of London development. But there's nothing like early successes to introduce early paranoia; i.e., delusions of granedur. Had they consolidated their success in 1959 by appointing an experienced professional team of City of London consultants to take it from that point, there might well have been a quicker and cheaper Tower in our midst before another half-a-dozen years had passed.

Instead the Board must have decided that, having got that far on their own, the rest would be child's play. And then they could boast of doing it all in-house without shelling out astronomical fees to armies of 'Olympians'. 'After all,' was the theme, 'don't we have our own Premises department here at National Provincial, complete with salaried architects, engineers, surveyors, and all that jazz! If we use them we can waffle over our decisions as much as we like and still save money.' Bankers are not to know that so many of those who are comfortably ensconced in long-standing staff appointments, don't have the same fire-in-the-belly as their hungry brethren in private practice.

Little wonder that it took all of four years before the first designs reached the stage where planning approval could be sought. The proposed development consisted of a speculative high-rise office tower, a new headquarters building incorporating the City branch, a new Club, some shops, and a pub.

When it reached the Planning Committee little time was wasted in reaching a decision. The application was rejected out of hand. The politicians killed it effectively by declaring that 15 Bishopsgate and the City of London Club were listed buildings, with preservation orders on them both. Neither of them were listed on the day the applications were placed on the G.L.C. commmittee table (or L.C.C. as it was then) but both were added to the list of inviolate buildings on the following morning!

In October 1963 an Appeal was lodged.

In November 1964 the Bank won half their drawn-out battle. Outline planning approval was granted involving agreement to demolishing the City of London Club, but the preservation order on 15 Bishopsgate was to remain.

The politicians were not to be outdone. The very same day that the National Provincial Bank won their appeal, the Labour Government introduced Office Development permits; which meant that the maximum office development that could be started without a Government permit must not exceed 3,000 square feet. Socialists could work at lighning speed if necessary, if the outcome of their efforts could be seen to spread plenty of egg on the 'unacceptable face of capitalism'!

As National Provincial's plans for the site ran into nearly 900,000 square feet, an application for an Office Development Permit was made early in 1965, and there the matter had to rest for another three years until the long-awaited permit arrived in June 1968.

Early in 1968 plans were announced to merge Westminster, National Provincial, and District Banks into one National Westminster Bank; with the former's highly efficient in-house design team taking charge of all Premises management matters once the proposed merger had been ratified in Parliament. When Westminster's in-house design team looked at the history of the H.Q. site project, still in limbo after nine years, they must have expressed opinions on the hitherto handling of the Tower project and requested that top full-time consultants be brought in by the time the merger became official for the Westminster team to take charge. In all probability they may even have nominated which professional practices to approach.

National Provincial's 'backroom boys' were thereupon put out to grass and Siefert and Partners, one of the most dynamic architectural practices in the City of London, were appointed toward the end of 1968. An equally reputable engineering consultancy, Pell Frischmann & Partners, joined the new design team. But besides inheriting the badly mauled project, they were also obliged to accept, though somewhat reluctantly, an appointed main contractor and an appointed electrical & mechanical services sub-contractor. Both had been given blanket orders by 'Dad's Army', long before there were any detailed designs whereby competitive quotations could be sought.

As already stated elsewhere, the prime objective for an experienced 'hunting' contractor is to befriend an overworked, lazy or incompetent consultant. Favours can then be exchanged, whereby contractor does a lot of consultant's design work and gets the job on a plate in return.

Be that as it may, the Client-hat was transferred from National Provincial to National Westminster on the 1st January 1969, when the new bank officially came into being. During the ten years preceding its birth the City planners had not been idle. They had their own views on how the development should be shaped, whereas the bank had never clearly defined its needs. It took 18 months from the appointment of the new design team to get detailed planning consent. In the meantime a public exhibition had to be held in the Royal Exchange to get reactions to alternative schemes, and a charge of £500,000 Development Tax paid under the Land Commission Act 1967, for the arrangement with the City of London Club. None of which need to have happened if the 'fiddlers' in Nat. Prov. had appointed professionals back in 1959. The Tower might well have been up and occupied by 1964.

As it was, demolition didn't start until July 1970.

National Provincial's Tower was to be a speculative development. Their Head Offices were to be sited in another position on the two-acre site, and the Tower would be a distinctive City feature as a magnificent office block let out to favoured tenants. The Old Banking Hall, situated on 15 Bishopsgate, scheduled for preservation as a building of outstanding architectural interest, would have to remain untouched. (In point of fact, toward the end of the project, it was restored in all its original glory as a museum, and re-named National Westminster Hall.)

When the merger took place and it all became NatWest, it was decided that 'The Tower' would be the new corporate H.Q., and that the lower dozen or so floors would be sufficient for that purpose. The Bank's administration, currently housed in a number of separate buildings in and around the City, could all be transferred into those 12 floors and the remainder rented off as previously planned. Another good idea that never got off the ground.

The old Westminster Bank Limited had set up an International Division prior to World War II, but had only a couple of branches in Europe by the time of the merger. The new National Westminster set about becoming international bankers in earnest. No longer would it stay content at being a domestic collection of 3,000-odd High Street 'put-and-take' shops, with indigenous banks abroad to represent its interests when the needs arose. Instead, it would put the name 'National Westminster' on the front of an imposing building in the centre of each of the world's leading cities. With this in mind, International National Westminster Limited was formed, with its Head Offices at 41 Threadneedle Street.

This one got off the ground so well it never allowed its preceding paragraph to take off!

Once the Tower was finished, said the bankers, International could move into three of those upper floors that were going to be let. But International, like Topsy, just growed, and growed, and still growed. A lot faster than the building in which it was to be given a home. Those three top floors became six, then ten, and then twenty. Nor did it stop there.

It became clear to the Bank that its image internationally was of more importance than it was to us on this Island, especially as success bred success and its profits in the International sector gave a healthy boost to the Bank's overall trading figures. Twenty floors became 30, 30 became 40, until, finally, the whole building was not going to be big enough once it was ready for anybody to move in. All this while 'The Tower' was slowly taking shape.

A preliminary scheme was set in motion for a second Tower to be built. As this did not get off the ground, the parent National Westminster Bank plc sentenced itself to permanent exile from the vicinity of 'The Tower'. Its administration would continue operating from several outlying offices even after the builders had finished, and its headquarters would remain at 41 Lothbury. But it was still Client as far as 'The Tower' was concerned, with International to be it's single-letting tenant.

Despite the difficulty of coping with Client's ever-changing decisions, work progressed until the steelwork of the Tower was complete. Then Client threw a really big one 'in the fan'! Somebody had told him that, in high-rise office blocks throughout the world, owners or principal lessees would house their most prestigious members in spacious and sumptuous offices sited on the topmost floors – not among the hurly-burly of the lower ones. After all, splendid isolation with superb views are the unquestionable grace-and-favour perks of those who dwell in the 'corridors of power'.

Client therefore asked for the steelwork to be altered to provide loftier offices on the top two floors, and a grand winding staircase built internally to link them. After all, Board members and illustrious guests could not be expected to wait around for lifts in order to visit between floors, and the starkness of emergency stairs on the sides of the lift lobbies ruled them out of the question for use by 'top brass'.

The design team fought hard, pointing out the structural alterations, prohibitive costs, and further delays these latest changes would involve. Client was indifferent to structural problems or additional costs, his attitude being much the same as it was throughout the project: – 'If I want something extra, and am in a position to pay for what I want, then why can't I have it?' It was explained that even after the calculations for the steelwork alterations involving the raised ceilings were completed, it would still be necessary to have them agreed by the authorities, and to have the changes approved – with resultant delays – before any new orders could be given to the contractors.

Eventually a compromise was reached. The ceiling heights could remain unaltered, but internal steelwork was to be adapted as necessary to allow a grand, winding staircase to go in. That was quite a costly variation in itself.

And so it went on. The project was not an easy one. The Tower is a unique tribute to British design and engineering, and as experimental in its way as the Hongkong Bank was. Another Concorde-type development to which nobody in all fairness could have attached an accurate price-tag in the beginning. So much had to be learned as the job progressed, and costly changes in both time and money were a regular feature. But far too many were due to bankers introducing changes after initial decisions had been made and implemented.

So much so, that when NatWest again wanted to don the Client-hat for a Management Studies & Computer Centre in 1979, on a site in Aldgate about the size of Trafalgar Square, the in-house design team told the bankers to keep out of the way until they had the original project finished. If changes were to be made they would have to be done afterwards and form part of a separate contract. The job finished as planned in two years, but once again the final cost, I am told, was way over the budgeted figure.

With regard to the NatWest Tower, Client 'fiddled' himself out of his Central Head Offices, outdated and overcrowded though they may have been, and went through 22 years of 'blood, tears, toil and sweat' to build himself a unique landmark of an H.Q. Only to find himself evicted into a number of separate buildings away from his landmark by a voracious young 'offspring', who thought 'his dad's new suit would fit him better!'

Wouldn't call that a very smart bit of 'fiddling', would you?

Having reviewed the failings of Bankers in the hard light of a 'fiddling' Client with ever-changing needs to suit ever-changing whims – and a bottomless purse to pay for them – there is the other side of the coin to consider. Sophisticated monuments, such as the National Westminster Tower, would never see the light of day if there weren't public-spirited and wealthy organisations willing to venture into the unknown to provide them. Their in-house team spared no expense or effort in researching the world in pursuit of high tech. so far untried at home.

I'll close this long chapter with some mind-boggling statistics about 'The Tower':

1. It consists of 130,000 tons of concrete and structural steel, mounted on a reinforced concrete raft 180 feet in diameter and 15 feet thick. Reinforcement consisted of 26 layers of 40-mm diameter steel bars, with a total weight of 2,500 tons.

   The raft is 60 feet below street level, supported by 375 steel piles – each 4 feet in diameter – driven down a further 80 feet into London clay.

   It has been calculated that it would need a wind-speed of 99 miles an hour to create a movement equivalent to half the thickness of a safety match!

2. To meet with planning requirements regarding available daylight, the office areas had to be cantilevered off the central core in three wings, each starting at different levels. They created considerable problems in both design and construction, involving complex jacking and scaffolding systems developed by Main Contractor to cope with them.

   The tower is claimed to be the tallest cantilevered building in the world.

3. The central core includes 21 high-speed lifts, five of which are double-deckers. The team visited the 1,400-foot high Sears Building in Chicago to study the system, before deciding that 'The Tower' would be the first to have double-decker lifts in this country. They run non-stop to the double-decked Sky Lobby on the 23-24 level, where passengers alight to board lifts to the upper floors.

4. The 132,000 square feet of tinted non-reflective glass windows are cleaned by an automatic washing system designed in the United States, and operated from a push-button control system on the roof. The washing heads travel on rails concealed within the 8 miles of vertical steel mullions, and the cleaning water is automaticllly filtered and re-cycled throughout the process.

   It was unfortunate that the only fatal accident throughout the whole Tower project occurred during the final commissioning of the window-cleaning equipment, after the completed building was officially handed over.

5. Heating, ventilation, and air conditioning equipment throughout the building is maintained at correct environment levels by a computerised automatic control system. The four 13-ton main boilers were hoisted to the top of the Tower by specially designed lifting equipment, instead of being sited conveniently somewhere down in the basement. Fumes were thereby discharged into atmosphere at non-pollution levels without the need to run heavy ductwork 600 feet up the building.

6. A fully automated railway system delivers and collects post and paperwork at distribution stations on every floor.

These are just a few of the fascinating features. Those interested in knowing more should either visit 'The Tower' or write to its Publicity department for some literature.

   Yes, having overcome the problems of those 22 harrowing years, National Westminster are to be congratulated on their magnificent edifice, clearly visible from my home in Hertfordshire some 16 miles away, with the hope that my closing paragraphs might compensate for some of those earlier 'nit-picking' observations!

There ends the story of two banks, 8,000 miles apart, but joined with an observation common to both. Bankers have the financial muscle to be unselfish in providing the world with expensive architecture and engineering in advance of our time. Having launched a worthy project and passed it to the professionals, they should then get down to making more money in order to finance even worthier construction schemes. They should be discouraged from site involvement except for foundation-stone, topping out, and handing-over ceremonies!

13

How to be a Super-'Fiddler'!

No, the real 'fiddler' is the professional Property Developing Client. The one with a network of 'spies' nicely planted and one ear always close to the ground. His stock-in-trade is vacant land and shabby old properties that bring in a bit of rent until he thinks the time is ripe to build. It could be a speculative development anticipating a demand for more rentable space in the area. He'll hope to sell the idea to a bank, investment trust, or pension fund while the work's under way. If they consider the deal worthwhile they will agree to buy the building from the 'fiddler' when it's finished, and find a tenant willing to pay a rent that compares favourably with what the purchase money would have earned if invested elsewhere. It must be a single tenant for the whole building, who would be responsible for sub-letting those floors not needed for its own purpose.

Alternatively, 'fiddler' may have heard that P.A.G. lost a site recently where it was hoping to develop its own head offices, and was currently on the lookout for one where all the preliminaries were completed. It didn't want to get involved again in another round of crossfire over acquisitions, and was desperately anxious to move into a custom-built high rise office block without the kind of 'hassle' it got mixed up with last time.

Or it can just be that P.A.G.'s Chairman has got enough sense to avoid a 'last-time' and tells the Board that 'horses-for-courses' is a wise maxim.

'Let's stick to selling insurance,' he says, 'where we know we can make money – instead of dabbling in

Property and Construction, where we can lose a packet. Let's find a professional developer able to offer a site of the right size and in the right position to suit our needs – something that already has outline planning permission with an agreed planning gain, and see what he'll charge to put up our new building and how soon we can have it. Then we can shop around among the professional "fiddling" fraternity to see which of them comes up with the best deal!'

Now that's the sort of decision made more and more by the amateur developer in pursuit of a one-off construction venture. With the result that the professional 'fiddler' hunts for prime sites against strong professional competition, and uses what can be compared to market-trading tactics when a potential customer comes to call. Picture the scene:

Seated in 'fiddler's sumptuous office and sipping chilled Krug from a Waterford crystal glass, P.A.G.'s Chairman describes what sort of onyx building he has in mind and the part of town in which he'd like it built. 'Fiddler' says, 'Don't go away. I'll have a word with my partner and go through the files to see what we've got that's not already under negotiation elsewhere. It seems everybody's gone mad on building new office blocks in the City!' He comes back rubbing his hands and a self-satisfied smile on his lips.

'It's your lucky day, mate,' he confides. 'I've only got one left and somebody left a deposit on it. But I see the option's expired this morning. If you care to sign up before you leave here today it's yours. It's just what you're looking for – a nice little plot with ready-made outline planning for up to 25 storeys and a deaf-and-dumb school. You'll have to give 'em that as a planning gain.

'My architect and Q.S. can call down at your place tomorrow morning and get some details of what sort of building you're after. Then we'll work you out a few alternative designs and prices. Once you've decided and agreed the figure it won't cost you a penny more unless you start wanting changes.

'You can move in 24 months from signing the order. We've already got outline planning as I said, and unless you come up with some weird ideas in the design stage we don't anticipate any difficulty when it comes to getting approval for the building. My boys have got good friends up at the Town hall. We've tied up with all the utilities for electricity, water, gas, drainage and telephones, and test-bores have shown it's a nice stable base for piling.

'Now how do you want to pay? We can fix it up for you through one of the pension funds, or you might want to do it on your own – seeing you're in that sort of business yourself. You can save money by paying cash up front, or if you like, pay us when we're finished. But the price will go up by a couple of million if you leave it till then. There's other ways you can do it in stage payments, and it's all set out clearly in this little booklet.

'You want to talk it over with your mates? Well don't be too long 'cos there's a big demand for this size of development. I wish I could get my hands on another half-a-dozen sites like it. Just send me round your cheque for 20 grand when you get back to your office and I'll give you a seven-day option.

'Good afternoon, and it's been a pleasure talking to you.'

Some might think that a bit of over-simplification. But the world of property-dealing is a complex one, which makes the action much easier to follow if geared down to a used-car dealer, or Arthur Dailey, style of sales patter. Anyway, it helps me to understand it all a lot better after converting it into plain bargaining talk – and even if I don't sing all the words right, the tune should be recognisable!

If P.A.G. had gone along with Property Developer's spiel then he wouldn't have worn the Client-hat for his project. P.D. would be Client, engaging 'hunters' through his own team of 'Olympians'. Or hiring tried and trusted private practices to do a traditional or management construction job – depending on the type of project in mind.

Some developers own separately run construction outfits, which are still expected to 'hunt' competitively if they want the parent company's business.

The 'Fiddler-on-the-Roof' hunts for customers to buy his land developments, but considers selling to be the simpler side of his business. Mark Twain once said that when his father was on his deathbed, he told his boy, 'Buy land, son, there ain't never gonna be any more!'. That was in 1847. The shortage is a lot more acute now than it was then, the demand is greater, and the price never stops rising. There's more and more would-be speculators looking for it, but only the top master-'fiddlers' can hope to succeed in getting hold of anything worthwhile. They're usually the ones with a bit more imagination and perseverance than their fellow 'hunters'.

Nigel Broackes, Chairman of the Trafalgar House Group, wrote his autobiography, *A Growing Concern*, in 1979.

Anybody getting as far as here with this book might get the impression that Trafalgar commissioned me to write it, or made it worth my while to shower them with free publicity. Well it may look like that but there's been no offers so far. I'm not sure if they'll even buy a copy come publication! It's just that having come in contact with many of their people so many times over the last 15 years of my business life, there are a lot of useful examples and anecdotes on the subject of 'hunting' that relate to them. And when it comes to describing the 'hunting' procedure of a top master 'fiddler' I don't know of a better source of reference than *A Growing Concern!*

I bought the book soon after it was published to give to my son-in-law for Christmas, but made sure to read it first. Some of the author's references to Victor Matthews, seemed a bit clinical, but what I remembered most vividly were his 'true confessions' on how smartly he worked when first entering the property 'hunt' in his early twenties. So much so, that when it came to drafting this chapter, I borrowed the book back to read the first half again; and again; and yet again. By the time it gets past half-way, the author's interests, ambitions and achievements take him well beyond the world of property wheelin' 'n dealin'. But a lot of that first half comes into the context of these pages and is well worth re-telling. Not presented in the detailed style with which he tells his story, but condensed and paraphrased to suit mine. Nevertheless, there's still a lot of it.

To understand what made him tick so successfully it's best to go back quickly through his early days.

Born in July 1934, Nigel Broackes was an only child of a Wakefield solicitor and an artistic mother. Each of his parents was an only child, too. His father joined the Army before World War II and died on active service on 1st January 1943. He left a total estate of £38.

But once he reached 21, Nigel Broackes was to receive a legacy of about £30,000 left to him by his grandparents. In the meantime the money was invested by trustees, and the interest went to pay for his education. This consisted of private day and boarding schools until the age of 13, when he entered Stowe, the public school near Bletchley, Bucks.

By that time he had already started in 'business', knocking-up radio sets from war-surplus parts and circuit diagrams in *Wireless World*; selling them for about a fiver, and making 100% profit. After three years at Stowe he'd had his fill of being a schoolboy, and left, after a bit of a row with the authorities, to become a junior clerk to a firm of underwriters at Lloyds. He was 16½ at the time.

With his mother and stepfather living in Devon, he lodged in a furnished room at Notting Hill, paying £4 a week from a salary of £220, and £250 a year from his legacy. At weekends he would join the family. Among some of the dodges he devised in order to live within his income, he describes taking the emergency stairs to get out of Notting Hill Station and using the return half next day; and an infallible system he'd worked out on greyhound racing that earned him £1 a day, six days a week, without fail.

After nine months with the underwriters, he started his national service and enjoyed soldiering with the Hussars in Germany. He was 19½ when he returned to Lloyds, but within a few months decided to leave. The ensuing year was spent planning a future, based on the £30,000 legacy that was to become his at the end of it.

He felt the development of war-torn Central London had prospects and, while waiting for 21st July 1955, bought and studied everything he could find on Company Law, Landlord and Tenant Acts, the current Finance Acts, together with most property and financial periodicals.

By the end of 1957, he was married, his first child was two months old, and he was 'skint'! He'd done his £30,000 in two business ventures! £20,000 financing a couple of blokes starting an injection-moulding plastics business near Bagshot, where they finished up having 70 people working the plant 24 hours a day, 7 days a week; plus about 150 outworkers. They made cheap plastic toys, and parts for Ford – but of course, were too cheap and the money ran out.

The other ten grand went through a finance business he started almost as soon as he got his hands on the legacy. Discounting H.P. to used car dealers and to 'tally' men (door-to-door operators selling household goods and clothing on the basis of delivery after a 5% payment and the balance, plus interest, over the ensuing 19 weeks). Although he gave it more time than the plastics business – a business that looked so good, until it was too late, that he'd only spend half-a-day a week there – those car dealers and tally-men finished up taking him to the cleaners about the same time as the other one folded.

As he said, 'There's no substitute for experience' – and paid nearly all he inherited for his!

To raise capital for further speculation he sold the lease of the Knightsbridge house in which he lived with his wife and baby, and moved into one of a block of flats above shops fronting Kensington High Street. This provided him with about £4,000 to play with. Prior to that, and before his first 'empire' had completely crumbled, he invested in 60 bubble-gum machines sited on forecourts of small shops around South London, and did the rounds every day collecting the pennies they'd taken!

He helped two friends to set up an estate agency partnership with other people he knew, and was paid £1,250 a year to manage a part of it from its Curzon Street offices. This, too, was while his first two ventures were tottering. He spent a great deal of his time there in studying and mastering the mysteries of valuation and surveying.

The partnership would buy up neglected or cheap residential properties in West London, refurbish them, and sell them for a quick profit. As time went on they relied more and more on young Nigel Broackes to put the scheme together and deal with all the legal, financial, architectural, surveying, and marketing aspects.

But the real money was in commercial, not residential, property and this was the direction in which he wanted to go.

At the age of 24, he saw a hidden 'goldmine'. It involved the partners buying the office block in which they worked, at its full investment value. But it wasn't for investment purposes that he pressed them to borrow the large sum needed for the purchase. The 'crock-of-gold', in his eyes, would be at the end of a 'rainbow' created by a full-scale property deal.

There was at the time a curb on new office development as, in their wisdom, the authorities wanted to deploy the Capital's industry, commerce, and population to the provinces. Long afterwards of course, in their belated greater wisdom, they decided to try to reverse the procedure, as within a few years London had become a ghost town of deserted buildings, with many of the home-grown population gone away for good.

Under the planning laws at the time in question, an

existing commercial user would have to be compensated if the authority refused him re-development of his own property. The maximum re-development the law would allow was 10% over the original cubic capacity of the building. But the office block in which Nigel Broackes worked was an old mansion with over 16 feet to the ceilings on the lower floors, and wide corridors and ceilings all over. A redevelopment with 8½ foot ceilings and a reduced width of corridors and stairs, would almost double the letting area of the building. It would be a bold Planning Committee to refuse consent and invite a hefty bill for compensation because of that refusal.

The partners were not too keen to believe young Nigel, but he was confident and continued to press his point. Namely: first buy the freehold of their office building, then apply for redevelopment consent, and then sell to a developer at a handsome profit when they got it. A partner promised him one-third of his share of the profit if it came off. Shrewd Nigel had that put in writing while euphoria filled the air. It came off, they sold, and his one-third share was about £25,000.

Prior to this, and while still a manager in the estate firm, he did his first 'solo' performance in property – a bombed site near Marble Arch with permission for six flats and a maisonette. Having raised money needed for the development with the help of a pal in Barclays Bank, his builders got involved in the work while he got caught up in a bit of discordant 'fiddling' with one of the partners in the estate firm.

They couldn't agree on the revised structure of two investment companies, in each of which Nigel was now to be offered a piece of the action and a part to play. The partner said he could come in on one or the other – Nigel claimed the preliminary discussions and agreement gave him entry to both. Disillusioned, he decided it was time he got out of their 'string ensemble' and started his own 'one-man-band'. So he gave in his notice and began to clear his desk.

It brought an immediate reaction from the others, ending up with him becoming managing director of one of the companies and withdrawing from the other deal. He paid £15,000 for a 42% stake – 10% down and the balance after a year. It was a nice little 'acorn' with a big name, Eastern International Property Investments (E.I.P.I.). There was a wholly owned subsidiary, E.I.T. Finance Company, to which he promptly sold his Marble Arch venture.

At the age of 24, he was now a mini-tycoon sitting in a mini-corridor of power. It was 1958, the assets of the 'acorn' were £66,000, and the reserves £23,000. Five years later he went public, having converted the E.I.P.I. 'acorn' into a 'young oak tree' called 'Trafalgar'. Trafalgar's balance sheet in March, 1964 showed six million pounds in assets and two million pounds in reserves!

The next chapter describes how masterfully a 'fiddler' needs to play to turn an 'acorn' into an 'oak tree'!

14

Seek and Ye Shall Find!

To be confident of access to big money, at acceptable fixed interest rates, is a must for any professional 'fiddler' in the property developing market. And the bigger the proposed deal the bigger the potential borrowing involvement. Life assurance and pension fund companies collect a lot of money in the form of premiums, which they then need to invest safely with good profit income – whereby fat bonuses and pensions can be forecast in their glossy brochures.

The Commercial Union Assurance Company (no relation to the Client-figure throughout this book!) was not much into property investment at this time. Through a friend who was a director of Commercial Union (C.U.) – and later to become the first Chairman of Trafalgar House – Nigel Broackes was introduced to their company secretary.

Over the next few weeks they had several meetings, at the end of which the C.U. paid £56,000 for 28% of the equity in E.I.P.I, and agreed to lend over half-a-million pounds in first mortgage debentures. In exchange for which, the C.U. company secretary was made a director of E.I.P.I, and helped open the door for Nigel's first big property 'fiddle'!

Before the tie-in with C.U., he wanted to know more about a block of flats in Knightsbridge that he thought were ripe for re-development and a possible two-fold increase in rents. By what he calls 'elementary techniques', he ferreted out the owner's name, Westminster & Kensington Freeholds Limited, together with the identity and site values of the other properties it owned – ten blocks of flats scattered around London, and three large old blocks of offices in prime positions. They were 110 Fenchurch Street, E.C.1; Cleveland House on the corner of St James's Square, S.W.1; and Trafalgar House, on the corner of Whitehall.

With the help of a company search he found that W. & K. belonged to an insurance company, called the North British and Mercantile, to whom he wrote expressing his interest in W. & K.; and got back, in return, what he called 'an unhelpful reply'. That was a few months before the meetings with his new-found friend, the C.U. company secretary, and now co-director on Nigel's Board.

It was at the last of that initial series of meetings, that he learned for the first time that Commercial Union had recently acquired the North British, and thereby now owned W. & K. They didn't like it very much because there were about 1,000 flats in all, of which many were let off at grace-and-favour rents to North British staff and their friends. The possibility of selling off W. & K. to property developers was now being considered, and Nigel was told that his interest would be borne in mind.

A few months later, his C.U. friend kindly provided the advance information that three developers, of which he was one, were to be given two months in which to prepare detailed proposals and bids. They were to be under strict instructions not to disturb the tenants, or resident W. & K. staff, who were to be kept in ignorance of a possible sell-out. This ruled out open visits and inspections. But Nigel Broackes got over that by classic cloak-and-dagger methods. To quote from his book:

> . . . I do not think our competitors can have penetrated as deeply as we did. In the case of the flats we got access [that friendly company secretary again?] to official records made for rating and schedule A purposes; so, with the additional knowledge of the tenure of each block, the accommodation of every flat, and the condition of a random sample visited

surreptitiously, it was not difficult to put a present value on each building, to estimate the costs of necessary renovation, and to calculate what the income should be, compared to what it was at the time.

. . . Cleveland House . . . had been requisitioned no less than three times for government offices – in the Boer War, and in both World Wars – and was still leased to the Ministry of Works . . . and Bob Chapman (an architectural colleague) enthusiastically set to work to see just what kind of office block we might produce on the site.

. . .There was no point in not telling Leonard [his co-Director and friendly C.U. company secretary] that, properly handled, this one property could be worth as much as the other 12 put together, but speed was desirable, and might be decisive. So, whilst the other calculations and negotiations continued, Bob and I were allowed to meet the Manager of W. & K., and his company secretary, on the strict understanding that we were concerned with re-development propositions and their assessment. [That is, commissioned by the C.U. to do so.]

I put in many weeks of extremely hard work on W. & K., preparing an illustrated report, and composed a bid which, though unorthodox, was to beat the others.

The whole deal cost the company exactly £550. Yes, for a total outlay of £550 Nigel Broackes won the freehold ownership of 13 highly desirable blocks of property for his Company! The actual financial details of the deal were: £3,335,000 to be left on loan by the Commercial Union, £9,000 of preference shares to be subscribed by C.U., £450 of equity to be taken up by C.U.; and the balance of £550 subscribed by E.I.P.I., to give them the majority 55% holding. Apparently the preference shares enabled ownership to be transferred without having to find the cash for £66,900 in stamp duty on the deal!

And if you think that's a feast of fantastic fancy-'fiddling', wait till we get to the next one.

Well, it's one thing having acquired a lot of potential development by some extra smart work, but coping with the construction programme itself, whereby the profit is to be made, calls for a lot of practical skills and experience. But first let's deal with the change of name.

Even before the W.& K. deal was done at the end of 1961, Nigel Broackes felt that Eastern International Property Investment Company Limited was too much of a mouthful even for a rapidly expanding company. As each of the 13 properties acquired with the purchase of W.& K. was registered as a separate entity, he chose the name of one that rolled off the tongue nicely, and sounded buoy-antly British. Thus Trafalgar House Limited became the name of the parent venture, and when they moved into new offices a little later he was pleased to get the number Trafalgar 1805 for his private telephone line. That was before the march of progress turned colourful exchange names into lots of meaningless S.T.D. digits.

With its brand new name and image Trafalgar was anxious to get on with renovating the thousand or so flats it now owned, most of which were in high demand areas, but somewhat neglected and dilapidated. Nigel's policy was to improve to a high standard and go for open-market rents. This needed a speedy system of instructing builders, without having to wait for specifications and tenders to be prepared. Three firms were invited to tender, on the basis of pricing up a Schedule of Rates for a random selection of flats, the winner to be given all Trafalgar's renovation work, and payment to be based on measure-ment by the Company's retained Q.S. against the builder's priced schedule. Bridge Walker Limited, of which Victor Matthews was Managing Director, put in the best bid. By the end of 1962, it was turning over about a quarter of a million a month with Trafalgar.

A couple of years later, a rival 'fiddler' made a bid for Bridge Walker that Victor wanted to accept. But first the bidder asked Nigel Broackes if Bridge Walker could still reckon on Trafalgar's work once he'd taken the Company over. He got a straight answer. No. Nigel reckoned the approach had been made behind his back some time after he'd introduced the said 'fiddler' to Victor. That was during a visit to Bridge Walker's H.Q., when seeking Victor's technical views on a joint venture the two 'fiddlers' were considering but did not complete.

The bid was withdrawn, and Victor complained that Nigel had sabotaged his one big chance of coming into money and living the life of Riley in the country! 'Never fear, Trafalgar's here!' was the soothing response and the Company promptly bought 49% of Bridge Walker from Victor for £64,000; with options to buy the remainder at a future date. It was not until 1967 that Trafalgar took up that option, by which time Nigel realised he needed Victor's management skills to earn money from his own entrepreneurial deals. The sale of the remaining 51% of Bridge Walker to Trafalgar made Victor Matthews his first million.

But to tell the story of Nigel Broackes' second big 'fiddle' on behalf of Trafalgar, it's necessary to go back to July 1963, when Trafalgar House Company Limited went public. The Head Offices of W.& K. had been in an old office block in Cannon Street, E.C.4. On one of his calls during the negotiations back in 1961, Nigel had noticed the name of the building's landlords, City & West End Properties, on the list of occupants in the entrance hall. They apparently shared the first floor, together with directors, shareholders, and management of two other property companies, Consolidated London Properties and Metropolitan Property Company. He made a note and started a few enquiries, hardly believing his luck in finding three firms similar to W.& K. at one blow; but better, because he believed they had more commercial, as opposed to residential, properties.

With his hands full of other things, it wasn't until he started organising the public issue for Trafalgar that he began 'hunting' the Cannon Street connection in earnest.

He spoke of his interest to the partner in charge of the stockbroking firm handling his public issue, which won him a big laugh. They were stockbrokers specialising in property shares, and knew of at least 14 previous would-be 'fiddlers' that had tried to 'play sweet music at the windows' of one or other of these old established companies, only to have a 'bucket of water chucked over them'!

Each of the three companies had enough shares in the other two to counter an attempted buy-out. A direct approach would be met with, 'What's your offer?'. The would-be bidder would reply, 'We'll need to assess your property values before we can figure a price, so can we have a list complete with rents, rates, tenancies, incomings, outgoings and all that jazz?'

Well the 79-year-old Chairman and his 81-year-old deputy had no intention of parting with their lovely old properties, and would tell each of those pre-Nigel 'hunters' that there'd be no disclosures until a firm bid was on the table.

But out master 'fiddler' was made of sterner stuff. First, he'd go for all three companies in one concerted bid, instead of making a play for one or the other. In that way, opposition from inter-company shareholdings would cancel each other out. It would need more money with which to back his attack, but this was promised from friendly bankers and the C.U., if his strategy were to succeed. First came the need to identify the properties – and it was the methods he used to achieve it that fascinated me.

Knowing that each of the properties would have at least one employee of the owners as a resident porter or maintenance man, Nigel mounted a secret surveillance on the Cannon Street H.Q. each pay-day. Making themselves as inconspicuous as possible, his amateur sleuths would 'tail' messengers taking wages out to the properties. There were lots of false scents and duplicated trips, before many months of perseverance established that there were a total of 70 London properties owned by the three companies. They were each surveyed quietly and professionally once located, and aerial photographs were taken to assess their size. With the use of large-scale ordnance survey maps, calculations for possible site development were made.

Then came a series of random visits to the properties by people pretending to call for any reason but the true one, which was to assess the internal decoration and nature of tenancy in each building. From these selective samplings, approximate rents and a fairly accurate value of each property could be calculated.

Needing to know which of the properties were freehold and which leasehold – and in the case of the latter how long the leases had to run – Nigel Broackes commissioned a 'fiddling' young lawyer to dig out the information for him. I mean nothing derogatory in that now-familiar term, although Nigel does admit that the smart work involved would not be allowed today. Apparently any solicitor was allowed to browse freely through the files at the Land Registry in those days, and providing he knew where to look, all the information wanted could be copied from the title deeds, including to which of the three companies each of the 70 properties belonged.

The whole exercise, in which up to 20 people were sometimes involved, was completed in total secrecy. Once valuations were calculated, Trafalgar approached the three companies with their initial bid at the end of October 1963. It was spurned – as expected. The battle lasted for ten months, and its outcome is best presented by again quoting from *A Growing Concern*. The salient points from his letter to Trafalgar Shareholders, dated 30 September 1964, included:

> . . . we have acquired City and West End, the largest and most desirable of the three companies, and have sold our shares in the other two to William Stern/ Freshwater interests and to Capital and Counties Property Company. We were able to offer pre-emptive

"Quarry left building turning East at 0945."

terms for City and West End because of the profit made on our shareholdings in the other two companies.

He went on to explain in his letter that the immediate effect on Trafalgar was that its net asset value, ignoring development potential, had increased from 37½p to 72p (he did it in the lovely old shillings and pence, but I've converted it as so many seem to prefer to think in pees today), and the value of their property portfolio had risen from £4.4 million to £10.9 million, despite some sales made to help finance the venture.

The Trafalgar House Group today is a huge diversified conglomerate, with 100 or more subsidiary companies outside of property developments. Its Construction division alone, under the heading of Trollope & Colls Holdings Limited, is expected to turn over something like £600 million in the year ending March 1986.

In 1979, Nigel Broackes was invited to lead the Dockland Development Board. A newly created Government body, its aim was to bring back industry and commerce to the deserted wastelands bordering both sides of the River Thames – from Woolwich up to London Bridge; an area that once bristled with hundreds of masts and funnels of the world's shipping – but now abandoned and derelict. This is due largely, I am told, to the development of larger ships and the increased expense of maintaining up-river wharfing facilities for them in tidal-waters; not to mention the never-ending exorbitant demands made by the men that helped load and unload the vessels. (I grew up, served my apprenticeship, and started my own business in those parts after demob from the Navy at the end of 1945. One of my first contracts was re-wiring Wapping's celebrated old pub, *The Prospect of Whitby*, in the summer of 1946. I remember it was summer because, after a pint and a pie at lunch time and providing the tide was right, some of us would dive into that murky old Thames from the verandah rail at the rear. And we survived, too!

The following year I moved to North London, and then to Hertfordshire. It was 30 years before I saw Wapping again, and remember how hard it was to reconcile memories of its once robust vitality with the desolate ghost-town that had taken its place.)

When Nigel Broackes accepted Chairmanship of the Dockland Development Board, he felt it a matter of honour to announce that none of his Trafalgar interests would be allowed to tender for the vast amount of construction work that the Board would help create. This didn't make him too popular with his own Construction division – pressed as they were to increase turnover on the one hand, yet, on the other, denied access to the huge, Government-sponsored growth areas along the Thames. Nevertheless, they must have had some consolation in 1984, when their boss was presented with a knighthood for services rendered to the re-incarnation of London's waterfront.

And, with the receipt of a title from a grateful nation at the age of 50, here is a fitting place to call and end to this saga of a grandmaster in the art of 'fiddling'. Well done indeed, Sir Nigel Broackes!

Before bringing this chapter to a close, I should make it clear that the Dockland Development Board, headed by Sir Nigel Broackes, had nothing to do with the re-birth of St Katharine Dock – a showpiece of environmental planning on a massive scale. That started 10 years earlier and is the subject of our next chapter – involving as it does another self-made super-'fiddler' of the Construction industry! The man, in fact, who advised the Government on the setting-up of London's Dockland Development Board, and was the first to bring private investment into that area.

15

Who Dares – Wins!

Contrary to popular belief, it was the Romans – not McAlpine, McNicholas, or Murphy – who built the earliest known settlement of London Town. That was soon after they first invaded Britain in 43 A.D. (The Romans, I mean, not the Irish!)

Boadicea burnt it all down in 61 A.D., but because of its strategic position on the River Thames it was rebuilt and surrounded on three sides by a great stone wall. The river, of course, forming the fourth side. By the end of the first century it was the fifth largest city in the western end of the Roman Empire, from all parts of which ships came to trade.

The north bank of the river between the two ends of the wall were soon lined with loading, unloading and storage facilities, and it was not long before the south bank was brought into play. Crude wooden bridges, built on floating pontoons, were used to link the two sides.

Soon after the arrival of William the Conqueror in 1066, he set to work and built the Tower of London at the south-east corner of its wall, thereby protecting the fourth side of the city from the usual run of pillaging, raping and looting, as practised by successive hordes of water-borne Danes, Jutes, Visigoths, Vandals and similar undesirable visitors to our shores over the previous 1,000 years. (It kept them out for almost another 1,000 but judging by the city's crime reports today, it doesn't seem to work any more!)

London Bridge, the first stone link across the Thames, was completed in 1209, and was soon crowded with dwellings, shops and a chapel arched over its central roadway. Despite fires and similar disasters, the structure lasted over 600 years. Until Westminster Bridge opened in 1750, it was the only means of pedestrians and traffic getting across London's river. John Rennie built a new London Bridge slightly west of the old one in 1831. As the capital expanded, and both river and city traffic increased, the need came for another road bridge further downstream and closer to the cargo-handling areas. Tower Bridge, the spectacular one with the impressive raising-and-lowering bascules, was built in 1886.

The story goes that it was Tower Bridge a wealthy American thought he was buying for a £1 million and a bit in 1967, when he heard that Rennie's masterpiece was to be pulled down because of structural cracks, with a wider one put up in its place. He rushed in to get his bid accepted, and it was – irrevocably. Having bought the comparatively unornamental London Bridge, he was obliged to have it shipped, stone by stone, and re-erected at Lake Havasu, part of a Disneyland-like complex in California. Another example of *caveat emptor*?

Since those old Roman times, ships would sail in on the tide, bringing their cargoes right up close to the London markets. As the centuries rolled along, vessels grew larger and drew more water, which meant they could not venture too far upstream. The banks below the Tower of London became lined with ship- and cargo-handling installations. Docking facilities were built, with lock-gates and deep-water basins whereby ships could get off the river, with its 24-foot rise-and-fall tides, and tie up against wharves and warehouses.

But until the early part of last century, about 25 acres of riverside London, just east of the Tower, played no part in the city's port activities. There was instead a hospital and chapel for those who dwelt in the parish. Endowed by Queen Matilda in 1147, it was accepted as a commitment by successive Queens of England to provide for the sick and poor of the teeming neighbourhood surrounding it. Queen Matilda named her bequest St Katharine-at-Tower, after Catherine, the patron saint of young maidens. (A young lady, apparently, who scolded the Emperor Maximinus at Alexandria in the year 307 A.D. because he was cruel to Christians, and was given her come-uppance by being tied to a spiked wheel. As the wheel failed to turn because of what appeared to be divine intervention, he had her beheaded instead. Catherine thereby achieved double immortality by (a), being sanctified by the Church, and (b) having a firework named after her!)

There was an ever-increasing need for more safe docks as merchants were bedevilled by problems of security and handling costs. Ships would lie at a mooring in midstream while waiting for an empty wharf-side berth to discharge their cargo and re-load, or else rely on shallow-drafted lighters and barges to ferry their cargoes to and from where they were moored. Night raids by low-tide pirates and pilfering from lightly-guarded wharves and warehouses had reached the stage when, in the early 19th century, merchants reckoned they lost 30% of their cargoes to thieves.

In addition, the vessels themselves were no longer safe at their moorings as, with the coming of steam, power-driven ships would charge up and down the river in search of the best berths or cargoes. In those halcyon days, there was no speed limit on waters that had catered exclusively for ships and boats under sail or oars, and many suffered damage through reckless or careless 'driving'.

Although still enjoying Royal patronage, and the peace and calm of the river's edge, the hospital and chapel of St Katharine-at-Tower was surrounded by horrific slums – by-products of water frontage in international ports since time immemorial. In 1825 a group of merchants bought the site, having convinced the authorities the area was no longer fit or safe for sick and poor people under care. They were to be re-housed in a new hospital in Regent's Park. The remaining 11,000 rag-and-bobtail that occupied the hovels, were left to fend as best they could when the newly-formed St Katharines Dock Company razed everything to the ground.

It took them about three years to transform the area into a complex of deep-water berths and fortress-like, fireproof warehouses. Like the Romans, 1750 years before them, they protected their three non-waterfront boundaries with a massive wall, 25 feet high by 3 feet thick, broken only by three heavily guarded entrances. Its security, compared to neighbouring docks, made it the objective of eager merchants with rare and costly goods to store – like ivory, spices, wine, rum, silks, perfume, furs. The walls may have kept the vagabonds out, but I remember working on the electrics there as a youth and still recall the exotic smells that filled the streets in those parts. As Lady Jocelyn, an eminent historian, said in her 'Historical Summary of St Katharine-at-Tower':

> A person with a good sense of smell could have found his way blindfold around the docks, past the rich hops from Hamburg, sharp cinammon, stinking hides, oranges, onions – and the rank smell of wild animals brought home by sailors and sold to the menagerie keepers of the notorious Ratcliffe Road that lies behind the docks; where you could buy a bear, a drink or a whore at any time of the day or night. The smells were unique, as were the neighbouring brothels.
>
> People teemed into the docklands of London from all over the world, and haggled, shouted, pilfered and bred all round St Katharine's. London was so much the home of seamen that children born on the high seas were registered as parishioners of Stepney.

In the same work, Lady Jocelyn reproduces part of a poem by John Masefield, England's Poet Laureate of the 1930s, and a great lover of all things connected with the sea. (I used to recite his 'Cargoes' to keep awake on watch during my own years afloat – as I did with other epic lines that pleased me – and still sometimes pass those boring motorway miles with what I still remember of that 'Quinquireme of Ninevah,' 'Stately Spanish galleon', or 'Dirty British coaster with a salt-caked smoke stack'.) He was taken on a conducted tour of St Katharine's Dock and wrote his appreciation to his host as follows:

> You showed me nutmegs and nutmeg husks,
> Ostrich feathers and elephant tusks . . .
> Cinnamon, myrrh and mace you showed,
> Golden paradise birds that glowed,
> More cigars than a man could count
> And a billion cloves in an odorous mount
> And choice port wine from a bright glass fount.
> You showed, for a most delightful hour,
> The wealth of the world; and London's power.

Came World War II and St Katharine's, like so many of our docks, took a hammering from which it never fully recovered. For the kind of reasons given at the end of the last chapter, the city's 2,000-year-old unbroken involvement with world shipping and cargo-handling, drifted 25 miles downstream to Tilbury. What was left of St Katharine's after the Germans and mindless vandalism had finished with it, drifted slowly into a long, deep sleep. The kind of sleep from which the only chance of awakening calls for a visit from some handsome and enterprising young prince.

Princes of any description are pretty thin on the ground these days – but lucky old St Katharine's got lucky again. In 1970 a man of vision saw the potential of restoring it to, and beyond, its former glory – but with an entirely different objective in mind. All that was colourful and nostaligic about the old St Katharine's would be retained, repaired, or rebuilt – all that was ugly or unwanted would be done away with. From it all would arise a modern complex modelled on the old, but bearing no resemblance to it in usage or purpose.

It took him the best part of half-an-hour to sell the idea to his boss – it was going to be a speculative development that would cost the Company somewhere around £100 million over the ensuing 15 years – but the boss was renowned for assessing possibilities and making decisions without waiting for his Board to ratify them. He was a professional. A super 'fiddler'! At the end of that half-hour the answer was 'Yes' – and Operation 'Sleeping Beauty' was launched in 1970!

Here's who did it, why, and how.

Frank Taylor was born in 1905, the only son of a retail greengrocer in Hadfield; a village to the north-west of Derbyshire, midst the foothills of the Pennine Range. He was 11 years old and still in short pants when his father had to take his mother to the coast for her health, leaving Frank in sole charge of the business. For several weeks he would get up at 4.30am to drive the horse and cart 11 miles into Manchester market and collect the produce; then get back with his cargo in time to open the shop at 8.00am. He left school at 13 to work full-time in the shop with his father, but continued his education by attending night school three times a week.

Because the bracing sea air was more beneficial to his mother's health than the fells of Derbyshire, the family moved to Blackpool; where, at 14, Frank got a job with a wholesale fruiterer. He learned to drive a model-T Ford and, although well below the legal age, his boss let him take the 7-ton truck to and from Manchester market.

It was 1919, and what was left of the nation after the horrors of the 1914-1918 war was trying to get back on its feet. Homes were a top priority and a boom in building began slowly to spread across the land. Frank took more than a passing interest and would help out on nearby sites after work. Then, at the age of 16 he borrowed £70 from his father, put his own savings of £30 to it, and twisted the arm of the local bank manager for the remaining £900 needed to put up a pair of semi-detached houses. One was intended for his parents and the other for his Uncle Jack, both of whom lived in rented premises at the time.

Working with friends and learning hard all the time, Frank applied himself to the craft skills of brick-laying, concrete-mixing, plastering, carpentry, plumbing, roofing; and, of course, the most vital of all – that of brewing up the site 'tea-boat' twice a day in a cement-encrusted bucket!

From the photograph of the house in a book called, *On Site*, by Alan Jenkins (to which – together with its sequel, *Built on Teamwork* – I am grateful for some of the factual information needed for my Frank Taylor story) they were a handsome pair of semi-Tudor-style houses. Unfortunately, neither of his kinfolk ever lived in them! They were forestalled by eager buyers who came along with their offers well over current market prices, and long before Frank had completed building them. He sold the pair for £1,000 each, making 100% profit on his total outlay.

That decided him. His future was in building – not bananas and Bramleys. He borrowed more money from the bank, although, having once proved himself, he didn't have to work so hard on the manager this time; even though it was a more ambitious scheme than the last. An estate of 20 houses was the target, and all were sold successfully with good profit.

Invited to a party at his solicitor's home to celebrate the 21st birthday of the latter's eldest son, Frank accepted gracefully and hoped the worthy gentleman would come to his own three years hence. The lawyer was horrified to learn for the first time that his enterprising young client was barely 18 years old.

'You're under age to be in business by yourself, Frank,' was the urgent cry. 'Get an older man into partnership with you immediately, otherwise we're both in trouble!'

'Will Uncle Jack do?' asked Frank.

On getting approval Frank approached his uncle, Jack Woodrow, to lend his name to the business. An office was opened on a housing estate in Blackpool, with the name 'Taylor and Woodrow' on its fascia.

It's now over 50 year since Jack Woodrow died, but – at

81 – Frank Taylor, now Lord Taylor of Hadfield, is still the very active President of Taylor Woodrow plc. With a turnover of well over three quarters of a billion pounds in 1985/6, the enterprising house-building venture that started in Blackpool in 1923 is now 150 subsidiary companies spread over five continents. Despite a Chairman and 18-strong main Board, all 150 are monitored by the President from his Mayfair office on a day-to-day basis – that's when he's not jetting off to Chile, China, Chicago, or wherever, to get the 151st under way! Tenacious old 'super-fiddlers' don't let go that easily.

Frank has always claimed that getting the right team together for any new challenge, and the resultant team spirit, is the formula for his firm's success. This he typifies with the familiar motif, or logo, of four stalwarts straining in unison at the end of a tug-of-war rope. Some of the huge civil engineering projects 'against which those four stalwarts have strained', include: dams in Colorado and Colombia; docks in Singapore, West Africa, Hong Kong; army camps, aircraft factories and the Mulberry Harbours of World War II; in addition to power stations, railway terminals, motorways, pipe lines, universities, hospitals, lighthouses, mines, oil wells, bridges, hotels, cathedrals, irrigation schemes, and so on, in all parts of the civilised – and quite often not so civilised – world. But it's just one of those Taylor Woodrow 150 subsidiaries – and just one domestic project out of all those far and wide activities – that brings their name into these pages.

In 1963, large areas of London were abandoned and derelict as part of the aftermath of war, and the Government thought it was time the place was tidied up. Many enterprising private schemes for development had been shot down by the restrictive policies of local planning committees – policies that were motivated more by party politics than by what was good for a particular area. The Government asked Frank Taylor to study and report on a possible partnership between private enterprise and local authorities, whereby large areas of obsolescent London could be brought back to life.

The idea was that the local authority would announce what sites it would make available and for what purpose (industrial, commercial, leisure, educational, residential, mixed) and find entrepreneurial developers to submit their ideas for building, at their own expense, what best suited the area. The developer to be responsible for finance, choice of tenants, and leasing arrangements – and the authority to give every assistance in planning and similar matters under its control. In other words, the builder would own what he built and be free to negotiate his own terms. Common enough these days, but before 1963 it was little known except for residential property.

One of Frank Taylor's team prepared a detailed report on the subject for him, showing advantages of the scheme, and quoted examples from the United States where it had long been practised successfully. It didn't take Frank long to appreciate the potential of working as suggested with local government and, in 1964, the Taylor Woodrow Property Company Limited was formed. Not specifically for the purpose described, but there's little doubt that the opportunities it presented helped Frank Taylor decide that property 'fiddling' was a natural spin-off to Construction 'hunting'.

St. Katharine's Dock, as described in the early part of this chapter, was one of the abandoned no-hope areas; it would need a huge amount of money, imagination and patience if it were ever to become a living part of London again. The Greater London Council were well aware of the problem. Early in 1969 they decided to hold a competition among developers, asking for proposals and designs for developing the area on a speculative basis. Schemes to provide for housing, commerce, leisure, education, links with the traditional past, and adequate approaches and car-parking – also to indicate what kind of employment the new development could generate among those that came to live there. Each competitor had to put up his scheme in detail, with all the usual small print and questionnaires studied and completed; examination papers to be returned to the Council offices by a given hour on a given day, three months hence, for study and assessment against the field. And it was quite a big field.

Peter Drew, a director of Taylor Woodrow Property Co., was a specialist in urban re-development. He had taken part in a survey of possible riverside developments on behalf of his firm, when the Government first asked Frank Taylor to study the problem. On being invited to partici-pate in the St Katharine's competition, he got a team together and tackled it, to the exclusion of everything else, for the ensuing ten weeks.

His finished plans included an 812-bedroom luxury hotel, a World Trade and Conference Centre, an exhibition and art gallery, a yacht marina, a maritime floating museum, schools, hundreds of homes, about a million square feet of offices, together with restaurants, shops, and underground car parks. All designed to retain the old nostalgic dockside atmosphere, and involving imaginative construction on a vast scale.

Before completing the official documents that would make his entry binding on the company, Peter took his boss, Frank Taylor, through drawings and descriptions of the scheme in detail, and all its financial implications. It took the old 'fiddler' half-an-hour to give it his unqualified blessing. 'If you win this one, Pete,' he said, 'it's your baby from inception to completion.' And he did – and it was!

On the eleventh hour of the closing day of the compe-tition, the project package was handed in to the G.L.C. to take its chance against a score or more of other entries. That was in May 1970. It was not until 25 November 1970 that Taylor Woodrow's entry was declared the winner. In a subsequent report acknowledging the interest of unsuccessful competitors and explaining the basis of assessment, they considered Peter Drew's plan different to the remainder in its creation of a Trade and Export Centre linked to a major hotel with all conference facilities. The hotel would also attract tourists and the development included special entertainment facilities for them. All of this, said the report, would re-vitalise the area.

There was, of course, no shortage of opposition to the scheme. Well, there wasn't to Concorde, either! Critics and rabble-rousers in politics and the press condemned it as unrealistic or capitalistic. Even on Taylor Woodrow's main Board there were those who said, 'Old Frank must have lost his marbles, letting that Peter Drew sell him this crazy St Katharine's idea! Who'd be interested in leasing an 800-bedroom hotel from us in scruffy old Stepney? It's the wrong end of Town for the tourist attractions of the West End.'

But in his calculations, Peter had taken into acount the £1,000-a-bedroom Government grant toward building hotels, aimed at increasing available accommodation and expanding the nation's tourist business. And when Lyons Strand Hotel Group decided to take a chance and come East, work on the new Tower Hotel started in July 1971. When opened in 1973, it was claimed to be the most luxurious in the country, and that every one of its 826 bedrooms overlooked the river or the colourful craft in the docks.

World Trade Centres originated in New Orleans, the second largest port in the United States. It was visited by a Japanese politician during the mid-1960s who, as chairman of the International Ports and Harbours Association, could see the advantage of a similar institution in every major port. But it was Peter Drew who, latching on to the idea and incorporating it into his prize-winning St Katharine's scheme, set the nations of the world off in following his suit.

Today there are 49 World Trade Centres in operation, 12 under construction, 33 planned and waiting to be built, and another 30 being negotiated. Having visited and enjoyed some of their facilities in Hong Kong, Singapore, New Orleans, and Dubai, I can sing their praises from experience. All magnificent new structures, they offer both home and overseas visitors every means of conducting their business affairs without any need to leave the building. Some of the services provided include: temporary offices, secretarial staff, reference library, telex, word-processing, photocopying, translations, language courses, telephone message handling, film shows and lectures, meeting rooms for up to 25 people, and of course, sumptuous bars and restaurants for members and their guests. International trade news and opportunities are regular features in the bi-monthly house magazine, as are the forthcoming leisure and other pleasant pursuits for the locality.

For less than £100 a year it is possible for a businessman to take up membership of his home World Trade Centre, knowing its amenities will be at his disposal in almost every trading country he decides to visit. Thanks largely to the enterprise shown by Peter Drew.

London's World Trade Centre at St Katharine's is built in the traditional style of the massive dockside warehouses that once stood on the site. But its facilities offer closer contact with far-away places than did the exotic goods once stored in those sombre old buildings.

The old dock basins are now full of colour, with an assortment of small craft tied to their walls, pontoons, and floating jetties – as befits a modern Yacht Marina, capable of berthing over 200 vessels of up to 100 feet in length. The Yacht Club, with its adjoining shower and toilet facilities, offer the capital's boat people, together with visiting mariners, all the comforts associated with modern small-craft havens. The original lock is still in use, but new lock gates, sills, and control mechanisms have replaced the war-damaged originals. Vessels can arrange to enter the dock or the river at any time within two hours either side of high tide.

Much memorabilia in buildings and waterways around the complex development go to form the Maritime Museum, and famous craft like the Nore Lightship, Scott's 'Discovery', old Thames sailing barges, tall tea clippers, and similar floating links with history, are – or have been – on display in the dock basin.

One of the buildings that escaped destruction when the St Katharine Dock Company cleared the site in 1825, was a free-standing, three-storey old brewery. They shored it up with drab grey bricks and put it to work as 'G warehouse' when the docks were opened. (I picked up a phrase in my youth, and have since used it repeatedly whenever needing to dive into another pocket in search of money, keys, wallet, or whatever. 'Let's check in G warehouse,' I'd mutter. The words stemmed from the old dockworker's idiom, but not until 'mugging-up' for this book did I figure out why G. It was because it stood on its own, a couple of hundred yards from the A to F larger buildings that, when anything went missing, the stock glib phrase would be, 'It must be in G warehouse!')

G warehouse had withstood the ravages of time and everything that Hitler sent over between 1940 and 1945, but was scheduled to come down to conform with the Taylor Woodrow programme. It wasn't particularly attractive, and, unfortunately, stood just about where the residential development was due to take place. When the wreckers were due to start, it was found that the bricks merely formed a shell over a handsome timber structure. Experts even estimated that some of the beams dated back to the late 15th century. The building would have to be stripped of its brick cladding and preserved, but the programme was stymied while it stood where it did. 'So let's shift it to where it won't be a nuisance and make a feature of it,' said Peter.

It was decided to shift the 150-ton, three-storey G warehouse about 50 yards, and position it to overlook the scenic entrance dock.

The building was loosened from its foundations, its timbers braced with scaffold poles, and Pickfords – the removal experts who claim to be able to move anything anywhere – called in. They spent the first day jacking up the structure to a height of 4 feet above the ground. Over the ensuing week they winched it slowly on rollers, and over sets of pre-laid steel plates, to its new position, where it was gently lowered on to a pre-constructed basement. It says much for the expertise of the 'Gentle Giant' (the marketing image of Pickfords) that the movement was so carefully controlled that not a creak or groan was heard from those old timbers – and a pair of nesting sparrows under the eaves hatched and reared a brood of fledglings while the warehouse was in motion!

The original timbers and wrought ironwork were brought back into play once G warehouse had settled into its new quarters, when it was transformed into a three-storeyed balconied-inn of the mid-Victorian period. And as Charles Dickens makes mention of St Katharine's in no less than 12 of his novels, it was opened to the public in 1976 by another enterprising individual, Michael Harwood, and named the Dickens Inn. The opening ceremony was performed by the famous author's great-grandson, Cedric, who arrived in a horse-drawn coach of the appropriate vintage and unveiled a bust of his great-grandfather on the entrance balcony.

Since starting on site in 1970, Taylor Woodrow has never ceased in its development of St Katharine-by-the-Tower – that now being the official designation of the area. A further link with the past will be established when Commodity Quay is completed early in 1987, to be handed over to the London Commodity Exchange as its centre for commodity dealing – plus individual private suites of offices for the tycoons who trade in that market. Commodities like coffee, cocoa, rubber, sugar, vegetable oil, were some of the staple cargoes brought in by the old merchant adventurers, to be stored in the warehouses of

St Katharine's and other London docks. The City institution that has long traded in them is now moving from its old market-place in Mark Lane, into a highly sophisticated development tailored especially to its needs; yet, once again, outwardly designed to resemble the old six-storey warehouses that once stored the world's produce in which it trades.

Just to the north of the old St Katharine's Dock boundary, stands what was the Royal Mint – surrounded by its massive thirty-foot walls. There has been a mint on Tower Hill since Roman times, but the last one was built in 1811, on the site of an old Cisterian monastery. In 1968, production of the nation's coinage, and a lot of the world's too, was shifted to South Wales. This chapter is being written in May 1986, when the Crown Commissioners first initiated the demolition and levelling of the five-acre site with a view to building another commercial and residential complex. Before they do so, archeologists are to be given their head for a period of six weeks, to rummage around for any small change of the past 2,000 years that might still be hidden in the old building's 'turn-ups'!

Since he prepared the concept of St Katharine's rebirth, Peter Drew has masterminded the whole thing. Praise and accolades have been showered upon him from many parts of the world, although every attempted progressive move set up its own wave of opposition. Mindless preservation societies, political activists, conservation groups, home-and-away hoodlums – all have created problems needing to be overcome. But his progress, despite setbacks and changes, is there for all to see. He considers himself a very lucky man to have had the handling of this unique and colourful development.

Some of his tangible rewards include: Chairman of St Katharine-by-the-Tower Ltd, Deputy-Chairman of Taylor Woodrow Property Company Ltd, Director of Taylor Woodrow plc, besides involvement in many other activities and spin-offs from the main project. He lives in a lovely old Regency house overlooking the river and the dock, once the grace-and-favour home of St Katharine's dockmaster, and works from his office in the old rum warehouse. He says he is still so deeply involved after 16 years, and so loves it, he feels he ought to pay Frank Taylor for letting him work there!

In both the books by Alan Jenkins, to which I am indebted for much of the factual information, a great deal of Frank Taylor's success is attributed to his faith in team spirit. Throughout his career he seems to have built up teams of dependable people, to whom have been given unstinting authority and confidence. Peter Drew's achievements at St Katharine's can be regarded as a tribute to the encouragement generated from the top by the No.1 team-leader – that one-time greengrocer-cum 'super-fiddler' – Lord Taylor of Hadfield!

The final chapter in Part Three is a complete reversal of everything that's gone before in this book. After an introductory preamble, it goes on to tell a story that is about as different from a conventional project report as Pisa's leaning tower is from National Westminster's straight one! Among other things it features:

A Client with no previous construction experience, but who set out to achieve a £10 million first-ever project without any funds.

An Architect who agrees to take it on when 'hunted-down' by Client, but confesses from the outset to no previous experience in that field of design.

A batch of hard-bitten contractors and suppliers who allow themselves to be bullied by Client into offering their services and wares without seeking much by way of reward.

A three-year project completed to an exceptionally high standard right on time and to original budget price.

And if you think that all reads like something out of Hans Christian Andersen, just wait until you get into the story proper!

16

The Exception that Proved the Rule

Frank Cherry was a fellow member of Crews Hill Golf Club, and a personal pal. He died in 1971, but his laconic turn of phrase and pungent wit have left long and fond memories. His description of a World War II experience is a classic example.

As a sergeant with the provost corps of a cavalry regiment, Frank served with the Eighth Army as it swept victoriously up the 'leg' of Italy. One of his duties was to skirmish a day or two behind the main troop movement in search of military skulduggery; like the sale of army equipment and supplies to civilians – whereby so many of our enterprising lads in khaki first raised the funds for a brilliant entrepreneurial future in civvy street!

Passing through a little Appenine village, Frank spotted a fine-looking, well-groomed horse grazing in a small fenced-in patch; with a couple of scruffy-looking nags of the local variety for company. He dismounted and knocked at the door of the cottage adjoining. A nondescript peasant answered and Frank asked in his best 'pidgin' Italian' who the horse belonged to.

'Iss mi 'orse,' was the instant answer with defensive hostility.

'This not your 'orse,' said Frank, slipping into the local vernacular. 'This 'orse belong English army.'

'Me buy 'orse from English army,' was the ready reply.

'English army not sell 'orses to civilians,' explained Frank.

'Me buy 'orse from English army,' insisted the churl. 'Me got chitty.'

'Bring chitty,' demanded Frank. 'Me shoofti chitty.'
(We're now into pidgin-Hindu!)

Pause while churl goes to rummage in drawer of kitchen table, to return with much folded and crumpled piece of paper. Frank carefully unfolds and straightens it out on the kitchen table. It is a sheet torn from an Army signal pad. On it was scrawled in pencil:

> If this bloke says I sold him this horse he's a !**!-ing liar!
>
> Signed . . . . Tom Mix.

('Tom Mix' wasn't too clever at spelling exclamation points or asterisks, so used the Anglo–Saxon equivalent – as did Frank when telling the story!)

Frank had served his apprenticeship in Construction as a craftsman in 'stick-and-rag' plastering, and was a rightful member of the Worshipful Company of Plaisterers. (That's the way they choose to spell it!) Rightful, because today all too many craft-less stockbrokers, solicitors, and commercial tycoons form the nucleus of the City's ancient Livery Companies,

At the time of his early death – only about 50 at the time – he was M.D. of a Taylor Woodrow subsidiary company, with a couple of factories manufacturing ceiling tiles and fibrous plaster mouldings; and he had an army of tradesmen working on Construction sites around the Home Counties.

Having golfed together one fine Sunday morning, we sat sipping that first delicious pint at the expense of our losing opponents, both of whom, too, were involved in some aspect of Construction. The conversation shifted from the valiant deeds that were wrought on the greens that morning to matters concerning our day-to-day struggle for existence. Somebody mentioned having landed a bit of action on a job where a Regional Hospital Board was Client, and wondered if any of us had experience of working with them. With intense feeling, Frank voiced the words that earned him the immortality of these pages:

'Working for a Hospital Board is no different to working

on a site with 22 bleedin' Clerks-of-the-Works!'

(Now one Clerk-of-Works per project is the normal quota – and as the status and duties of this important gentleman is worthy of further explanation, his role as Client's 'watchdog' is described in Appendix D.)

Frank quoted at length from his experience of muddle and indecision brought about by the 12 or so lay-members of a Regional Hospital Board (22 was a bit of an exaggeration to help make his point) on their monthly conducted 'walkabout' of a hospital building project. With picturesque language he described how they would be led by the design team, and followed by senior personnel of main contractor and major sub-contractors – much the same sort of procession that follows the top man on morning rounds in one of the teaching hospitals.

Although knowing little of the mystique of Construction, most of the Board members would find something to say about the quality, shape, size or position of what they saw, and suggest that a modification or alteration be made to perfectly good finished work; usually for no better reason than another of their number has just shown off elsewhere on the rounds and it's now their turn!

That's one example of why hospitals take so long to build, and finish up costing a lot more money than was originally budgeted.

Another reason is that all too often, despite a Regional Board having every intention of building strictly to plan and to time, the medical fraternity attached to the project cause delays. A great deal of high-tech equipment goes into a modern hospital. Every day, some research or commercial laboratory around the world announces a breakthrough in one or another field of medicine, usually involving new photographic, sonic, electronic or laser-beam apparatus that will need to be installed in a certain way. Doctors, specialists, radiologists, physiotherapists, all want the best and latest 'toys' built into their new hospital departments, and are loath to approve a layout – no matter how hard Architect is pressing for it – until satisfied it will accommodate gadgetry they've only just heard about.

There may have been a write-up in that week's *Lancet* about, say, something designed in a Latvian clinic, that will completely change all recognised treatment of, say, Korsakoff's Syndrome. (A complaint I picked at randon from the *Reader's Digest Family Health Guide*; but no doubt familiar to everybody as a mental disease, often caused by too much alcohol in the system. It's symptoms are memory blanks, and lack of understanding of time and place. When I told my wife she said I must have had it for years!)

Specialists in that field will insist on awaiting details of the new equipment before agreeing to how the Korsakoff treatment area is to be laid out. Now multiply that up by the number of entries in your medical reference book, and you get an idea of how many reasons there can be for delayed progress in the building of a hospital. Once open and ready to roll, nobody wants to 'carry the can' for an obsolescent area that failed to make provision for, say, a Mark Seven Anal Scanner; especially as it is now looked upon as standard equipment in every private-patients' clinic from Westcliff to Warrington!

All very laudable, but the increased construction costs caused by re-decisions and delays – whatever the reasons – play havoc with a Hospital Board's budget. It means their money runs out, causing other worthwhile causes to go to the wall, because of unproductive cash being used up as described. The Boards are then cast in the role of wicked and heartless 'Barons', when a much loved little rural hospital is closed down, because they can't or won't provide the funds to keep it in good repair and pay the wages.

Never was there a more classic example of this than when, somewhere around Christmas, 1979, the ceilings of five wards fell in at the Spinal Injuries Centre, Stoke Mandeville Hospital. Forty years-worth of rain-soaked plaster, dead flies, spiders and woodworm were deposited on the helpless patients below, who had to be speedily evacuated to other parts of the hospital.

Stoke Mandeville Hospital was built at the start of World War II, to be used for the treatment of war-disabled. Its Spinal Injuries Unit was opened early in 1944 – in preparation for the opening of the Second Front – to study and treat paralysis of lower limbs and trunk, and the attendant body-function complications. The medical term for this is Paraplegia. Tetraplegia is complete paralysis from the neck down. Five wooden single storey huts were built as temporary wards, with a possible lifespan of 10 years. Instead they lasted out for 40, specialising in treating and rehabilitating mostly healthy young people, suddenly condemned to spend the rest of their lives in a wheelchair if they're lucky – or in a bed if not – usually because of a motor-cycle, car, airplane, riding, or similar accident.

The Unit became renowned for its skills, and patients would be flown in from all parts of the World for treatment, plus the hard slog of psychological re-adjustment. On an average it would take about 12 weeks to get a patient ready for a wheelchair existence, involving limited ability to cope with the 101 daily functions taken for granted before the accident. After which would come a discharge from the Unit, with periodic return as an out-patient for monitoring and any further treatment that might be necessary.

Then the roof fell in! Literally.

The 'bold, bad Barons' of the Board said, 'Hard luck, but you've had a good run as a special unit and we've no money in our kitty to build you a new one. People needing this kind of treatment in future will have to look for it in their local general hospital. It may not have quite the expertise of this place in dealing with physical and pyschological damage caused by injury to spinal cords, but will no doubt learn to cope and ask for help when needed.'

Horrified at the closure of their old *Alma Mater*, to which they felt they owed so much, former patients arrived in droves that Christmas, and chained themselves and their wheelchairs to the empty beds in the derelict, weatherswept wards. Much publicity resulted therefrom on T.V. and in the newspapers. Volunteers brought in oil stoves, fast food takeaways, and all manner of drink to the brave squatters. The Minister of Health and his Regional Hospital Board received a lot of bad press over it, and the Government told him to get the squatters out. So he went down to Stoke Mandeville, with the usual entourage of V.I.P.s, cameras, and reporters, and appealed in vain for the paraplegics to abandon their forlorn cause. 'Your gesture amidst these appalling conditions do you proud,' he said 'but we just haven't got the £10 million it's going to cost to build what is needed here.'

Then up rode a 'Knight in Shining Armour', to parley with the 'Barons'. Better known to all as Jimmy Savile, a household name in the world of entertainment. After putting on a show in a fund-raising fête at the Spinal Injuries Unit some 17 years earlier, he went on to donate his free time on almost a daily basis in voluntary physical work there ever since. Stretcher-bearing, pushing wheelchairs, chatting to patients in the wards, or any portering task – somebody would just have to say, and Jim Would Fix It!

Said Jim to the Minister and his Barons: 'Look – you say that it's just because you don't have £10 million to play around with that we can't have a new Spinal Injuries Unit here at Stoke Mandeville. Supposing I set about raising that kind of money in a nationwide appeal – what then?'

The Minister was no mug in recognising a lucky break for his image in the resultant far-from-adverse publicity. He certainly wasn't doing very well in the ratings at the moment; what with the media bulging with pictures of paraplegics eating fish and chips under umbrellas while chained to rain-soaked beds. He put his arm round Jimmy's shoulders – figuratively, of course – and said:

'If you go ahead and do just that, you can not only have your new Unit but also, as you're going to be responsible for the funds, you can wear the No. 1 Client-hat. With your

17 years of working around the place nobody can have a better idea of what is needed here, and you have both the time and enthusiasm to pursue such information not already at your finger tips. The 'Barons' will be instructed to give you all the assistance needed, and heads will roll if you tell me that any of them has tried to wave just one-inch of red tape in your direction.

'But it's your ball-game from here on in, Jim baby, and we're all rooting for you!'

Now it's generally known that Ministers of Health don't quite speak like that – but it serves to summarise the discussions on ways and means that must have taken place at the time.

With the Minister's assistance, Jim wasted no time in launching his appeal from a packed Church Hall, Westminster. A Mr McMinn from Chesham, Bucks, gave it a grand start with a donation of £150,000. Excellent media coverage and Jim's constant reference to his cause in his weekly *Jim'll Fix It* programmes, had the nation solidly behind him. His disarming policy was simplicity itself. 'Form little sponsoring groups and go out and have fun. If you manage to find yourself with a bit of money left over, then send it to the Appeal funds.'

I have a list of over 200 different types of fun-seeking parties dreamed up by adults and children to raise money for his cause. Sponsored parachute jumps, three-legged pub crawls, field-gun pulls, dog-jogs, marble-rolls, sit-in-baths-of-spaghetti for a week, sausage-eating, wellie-throwing, haggis-hurling, beard-growing, Lands End to John of Groats walking, skating, or riding a road-sweeper, how many Smarties in a sweet jar, wine-gum chews, etc., etc.

He was repeatedly asked to be present, take part, present prizes, receive donations – but as he couldn't possibly accept every invitation he said it wouldn't be fair to accept any. Instead, he reversed the situation by organising Saturday and Sunday as Open Days twice monthly at the hospital. People would then come along and present their donations, meet patients, be given tea and get shown around on conducted tours by volunteer admin. and medical staff – or by visiting out-patients – while awaiting their turn for a chat to Jim. There were up to 1500 there on any one day, with entertainment and music making it, once again, a real fun time for all.

Well, it's obvious that Jimmy Savile knew quite a bit about raising funds for good causes; and just as obvious that he'd learned a lot about paraplegics over the previous 17 years. But he'd be the first to admit he knew absolutely nothing about building hospitals – or come to that, building anything. Nevertheless, with the Appeal well and truly launched, the time had come to think about constructing something.

A well-meaning friend told him that all he had to do was decide what sort of size, shape, and style of building he had in mind, and then go out and find an architect to do the detailed design. Once he'd agreed to Architect's proposals, the latter would take care of everything and all Jim would have to do is pay the contractors when called upon to do so.

He walked about Aylesbury and district looking for the sort of building that might take his fancy among newly built structures. The Post-Graduate Centre in Stoke Mandeville did just that. It was built of rich purple-hued bricks of varying shades, with a pleasing shape that spelled out comfort and warmth. A plaque on the wall named the architects – Fitzroy Robinson & Partners, of London W.1.

Jimmy Savile made an appointment to call and see their senior partner – our old friend Geoffrey Rainbird, who featured in the chapter on Sandown. He explained the history of the decision to build the new spinal unit at Stoke Mandeville, and his involvement therein. 'I took a fancy to your new building in the Town,' said Jim, 'and I'd like you to come and build something like that for me.'

'I'm very flattered,' answered Geoffrey, 'but I've never

ever been involved in the building of a hospital. It's a very specialised field. But I shall be delighted to introduce you to my opposite number in one or more of the architectural practices that are experts in that sort of thing.'

'I don't want specialists or experts,' said Jim, 'I want you! My patients are healthy people who probably never ever saw a hospital until – 'Wham!' Their first impressions and surroundings in the new Spinal Injuries Unit will play a big part in their re-habilitation programme. They will already have had at least one spell in a hospital before being sent to Stoke Mandeville. We want them to think of the place as a training establishment for a new way of life – not just another round of hospitalisation.'

He's a very persuasive talker, is our Jim, and in May 1980 Fitzroy Robinson & Partners were appointed officially as Architects for the project, with Geoffrey Rainbird now as eager as Client to get the job rolling.

Then came a most uncanny indication that the success of the venture was pre-ordained. When checking Jim's address for a quick contact at any time, it transpired he lived just off Harley Street, W1 – only a few yards from the mews flat owned by 'Geoff' Rainbird! Geoff lived and spent what time he could at his home in Sussex, but stayed at his town flat during most of the working week. He said he and Jim saved any amount of time through being able to get their heads together on the project long after offices had closed for the night.

Like the time when, in the early days, Geoff approached the Regional Hospital Board for a design brief on their standard and special requirements. After all, they were the Authority, and the building he was to design needed to conform to their specific rules, like dimensions of wards and treatment rooms, and the equipment to be fitted in them. The same applied to reception areas, kitchens, dining rooms, lounges, staff quarters, toilets, stores, etc. Besides heating, plumbing, lighting, electrical, security and safety needs, and so on. All involving hundreds of items with descriptive sketches and/or write-ups.

The Board were most co-operative. They'd been told about the urgencies at Stoke Mandeville, would give the matter top priority, and the complete design package would be ready for him in 18 months. Poor old Geoff was staggered! He mumbled something about he could hardly start without it, yet had been given a total of only three years in which to have the place completed and handed over. They explained patiently that it was only because they knew how urgently the finished hospital was needed that they'd pulled out all the stops and were able to quote him 18 months. It would normally take 2½ years to provide an architect with the sort of design brief he was after.

Sad and dispirited, Geoff called on Jim that evening and gave him the bad news. 'Leave it to me,' he was told, 'Jim'll Fix It!' Whoever Jim went to see the following morning had better remain a mystery, but later that day Geoff had a telephone call from the Hospital Board. The design brief it was going to take them 18 months to prepare would now be delivered to him by special messenger in six weeks! And it was, too – a thumping great package of it.

Then Architect told Client, 'Look, Jim, if we're to get this show on the road and finished in three years, we can't wait until you've got all your money collected or underwritten. Nor until I've got all my design drawings and detail finished so that we can go out for competitive tenders'.

'What are the alternatives?', asked Jim. 'Because I'd like to find some kind-hearted, prosperous builder that'll do it all for nothing. Or as near to nothing as a bit of good old-fashioned arm-twisting might get us.'

'Well', explained Geoff, 'bearing in mind it's size and proposed pace, I can't see you finding anybody around Stoke Mandeville able to handle it. One of the big London-based firms is what you'll need. You might be able to pressure them into making some kind of gesture, but a quick appointment is the first and foremost consideration. They'll have to work with me on some sort of controlled negotiated basis. That way I can get them into action without delay on initial site-work, and feed them piecemeal with construction detail as fast as I can churn it out. There's also no time for professional engineers to design the Services. We'll have to do that roughly the same way – negotiating with a sub-contractor we can trust to both design and install all the heating, ventilation and electricals.'

Before going any farther I should explain a bit of the real Jimmy Savile. Behind that façade of an extrovertish professional entertainer, with a line of disarming 'Yorkie' patter and patronising simplicity, lies a needle-sharp brain. Strictly T.T., he openly admits to a sense of satisfaction in his self-created image. 'As long as they think I'm stupid, I'm winning!' he says. What is not generally known is that he has an I.Q. of about 157 and is a member of MENSA, the elitist closed-circuit club of super-brains.

Having explained the kind of builder he wanted, Geoff was asked to write down a list of the top London-based people, with the name of its chairman or chief executive against each one. He thought up about eight, including names like Taylor Woodrow, Laing, and Bovis.

Jim went down the list, striking out one after another as he murmured, 'Never heard of them, or him', until he came to Trollope & Colls, with the name 'Lord Matthews' written alongside it.

His brow furrowed in thought. Then, 'Isn't he the fellow who runs the *Daily Express*?'

'Well, yes,' started Geoff, 'but he's also the top exec. at Trafalgar, who own Trollope & – '

'That's our man,' interrupted Jim, 'let's go and see him.'

Fortunately, Geoff Rainbird and Vic Matthews were old friends, having done many jobs together over the previous dozen years or more. Without giving too much away, Geoff explained over the phone that Jimmy Savile was anxious to meet him on a matter of importance, and was told to bring him over to Trafalgar's head office that morning.

Jim wasted no time in getting down to business when they were ushered into the sumptuous suite on the third floor at Berkeley Street. 'I want to give your firm this prestigious and publicity-laden contract for the building of my new Spinal Injuries Unit at Stoke Mandeville Hospital. On Geoff Rainbird's recommendation you can have it on a plate, providing you don't try to make too much profit out of us. In return I want you to run a nationwide appeal for funds through your Express group of newspapers. I'm getting money in from all sorts of gimmicky sponsored events, but only a newspaper like yours can give the Appeal the clout it really needs. With you as Chairman of the Appeal Committee, our cause will get unstinted support throughout the land.'

In vain did Victor protest that never a day passed but his in-tray and switchboard was besieged by organisers of similar worthy causes, seeking similar patronage. But Jim claimed that his was the whitest and worthiest, compared with which the claims made by others were no more worthy of notice than the barking of fairground hucksters.

As Jim persisted and over-rode each and every argument with which Victor tried to explain that it could not be done, the latter said, in desperation, 'All right, give me a couple of days to think about it and I'll give you a decision. Now please shove off and let me get on with some work.'

'Well, you tried hard,' said Geoff in the lift on their way down, 'but I doubt you'll have won him over when he does come up with an answer. He only asked for the time to get you off his back.'

But Jim seemed strangely quiet and self-satisfied in the taxi back to Geoff's office, where they parted company and went about their respective duties.

The following morning Lord Matthews received a personal letter on Buckingham Palace notepaper, expressing the deepest appreciation of his magnificent gesture in support of the new Spinal Injuries Unit at Stoke Mandeville!

(I.Q.s of 157 work in weird and awe-inspiring ways!)

That is how it came to pass that in May 1980, Trollope & Colls were appointed main contractors – and, in July, Lord Matthews became a Trustee of the Appeal he launched so successfully through the Express group of newspapers. Having accepted commitment, he threw all his efforts into the building of that Unit, with his usual single-minded determination.

My own involvement started when, shortly after their appointment, Trollope & Colls circulated their regular suppliers and sub-contractors. We were invited to signify our willingness to make some kind of offer or tangible gesture toward the building programme. Those who responded suitably were invited by the Minister of Health to a cheese and wine 'elevenses' at Admiralty House, where the 41 Construction 'hunters' present listened to good 'hunting' talk by the Minister, Jimmy Savile, and Lord Matthews. Only this time we were the 'hunted' ones, being asked to consider playing a part in the project and making some contribution toward the Appeal; and once having made our decision, to write to Trollope & Colls setting out clearly the financial substance of our offer.

Just to enlarge on that last point: gestures are often made by business people that they will do work at cost without adding profit. Or only add overheads or administration costs, leaving out a net profit. But there's an awful lot hidden in standing overheads, or in what might be considered an on-cost to a particular job. Overheads sometimes include accepted 'marketing tools' like a box at Ascot, an ocean-cruiser at Miami Beach, a flat in Paris. All charged on the books as aids toward winning export orders.

On the other hand, the 'at cost' offer can really mean what it says – the genuine bought-in price of materials and labour supplied to site, including the cost of getting them there. To which might be added a stated percentage to cover such admin. charges directly attributable to the job.

Quantity Surveyors, therefore, would be needed to calculate the true value of the various offers received, and to monitor quantities and prices during site progress.

Then there's the kind of handsome offer made by Crown Paints Ltd, who kept the project supplied with all the paint it needed at no charge. That kind of gesture doesn't call for the services of a Q.S. (They did well out of it, though: ever since I learned of their donation I've only bought Crown Paint products for my D.I.Y. efforts around house and garden, and am already half-way into a second 2-litre can of white gloss!)

Going back to the Q.S, those 'Olympians' associated with building the Spinal Injuries Unit at Stoke Mandeville also made handsome gestures with regard to their fees, and are worthy of mention. They are listed at the end of this chapter.

Chris Henry's gesture was somewhat similar to that of Crown Paints, with the result that on 16 June 1980, exactly a week after the meeting at Admiralty House, demolition and site clearance started, with plenty of T.V. and press coverage in support of the Appeal. Eventually, the completed and brand-new National Spinal Injuries Centre at Stoke Mandeville was opened by the Prince and Princess of Wales, with even greater T.V. and press coverage, on 3 August 1983.

Between those two dates there were no shortage of impressive examples of why this one went so differently from the most carefully planned, more-conventional programmes. I'll describe one or two.

Once work started on site, Jimmy Savile would wander around the wards where the paraplegic patients were temporarily housed, and press them to get down and make themselves known to the people working there. The complete area was enclosed by a chestnut-paling fence some 8 feet high, but they could see and be seen through the gaps between stakes. Daily, patients between the ages of five and fifty would wheel themselves down there and laugh, chat, or exchange sweets, fags and papers.

That was fine during the nice, hot summer, but once winter started to set in there weren't quite so many anxious to leave the comfort and warmth of the hospital building for socialising in the fresh air. One bleak morning Jim looked out at the deserted site perimeter fence, and then at the various groups sitting around and amusing themselves indoors. He called a number of them together and spoke:

'Listen to me. Those men out there are supposed to be building your new home. It's going to be the most advanced treatment centre of its kind in the world. The sooner they've got it finished the sooner you, and people like you, will get that treatment.

'Those men don't like working in rain and snow any more than you like going out in it. But every morning and afternoon, one or more of you must wheel yourself up to that fence and wave at the folks inside. And you're to stay there, waving, until you get an answering wave. Just wrap yourselves up good and warm, because you might have to wait a long time before you're noticed. When you are, and not before, it's O.K. to come back in here and get round the fire.'

And so they did, until came the day when snow and ice brought the uncovered site almost to a standstill. Just one fitter could be seen outside of the mess-hut, fiddling about with the 'innards' of one of the earth-moving machines. Huddled low against the biting wind, wielding a spanner and hammer, he paused to straighten up and look around the white and silent vista while trying to blow a little warmth into his fingers. A movement caught his eye through the palings. It was a small figure in a wheelchair, swathed in all manner of protective clothing, with a little half-bent arm poking up in the air. Bewildered by its presence, he walked slowly forward and spoke to an eight or nine-year-old girl through the fence. The conversation went something like this:

170

'Hello. What the divil are you doin' out there in this weather?'

'I'm waving at you.'

'What are you doin' that for? Is something wrong?'

'No. Mr Savile said we've got to sit out here and wave to you.'

'In the name of Heaven, why would he want you to do that?'

'Cause you're building our new hospital and we've got to wave to you.'

'And how long did Mr Savile say you had to sit out here and do that?'

'Until you wave back.'

'Well here's your wave back. Now get back inside before you catch pneumonia. No, just wait there another minute.'

He hurried back into the mess-hut and got some of his mates away from their tea-mugs and cards. They came out putting on coats and waving. With a final flutter of the hand, she turned her wheelchair and trundled back to the ward, from whence another patient then set forth for a waving stint at the fence.

Despite an appalling winter, there were little stoppages on site after that. Not with the knowledge that there might be a paraplegic or two hanging around for an answering wave or a chat.

Came the week-end when snow fell without let-up, and a new site agent was due to take over the running of the job. He arrived early Monday morning, looked at the white-encrusted vista, put the padlock back on the gate, and went into the hut that served as his office. A quiet, uninterrupted day was anticipated, in which he'd be free to study the paperwork of his new appointment. He'd hardly put the kettle on when there came a rattling from the lock and chain on the gate. About half-a-dozen 'paddies' stood there, shoulders hunched into their site-jackets against the weather.

'What do you want?' he asked.

171

'We've come to clock-in and work,' said one.

'You must be mad!' He was amazed. 'The job's unworkable. With 30 years in the industry I've never known anybody want to work on an open site in these conditions.'

'Ach, let us in,' was the reply, 'We'll find something to do. We don't want to be disappointin' those crippled folk coming out in their wheelchairs for a wave and a 'crack', do we?'

And so it went on. The men on-site would take their invalid pals down to the local pub for a pint and a game of dominoes or darts after working hours, run coach outings to the coast and safari parks at weekends, or on pleasure launches up the river. They ran a paraplegic welfare fund out of their wages, to which all who worked on site contributed. They organised raffles, sweepstakes, competitions and collections around their own homes, clubs and pubs in order to make donations to the Appeal Fund.

When two of their paraplegic pals wanted to get married, there were no facilities around the hospital for a bride-and-groom to enjoy a joint life of domestic bliss. Just the usual back-to-back individual rooms designed for single occupancy. So the boys took a little time off-site, knocked down the dividing wall between two of them, decorated and refurbished the enlarged flat, and had a whip-round the job to provide some colourful non-hospital-issue furniture as a wedding present. Not the sort of procedure normally approved of by the authorities, but those in charge sportingly turned a blind-eye on whatever infringements might have arisen from the good intentions of those warm-hearted Construction operatives.

But the pace, especially at the outset, was a killing one. Especially for the one man who had taken on the responsibility for converting a pipe-dream into reality. Geoff Rainbird and his team worked night and day on design work, drawings and specifications, on some of which the ink was hardly dry before being passed to the builders awaiting their next issue of instructions. Midway through that first winter and while on a business trip to the Middle and Far East, he picked up a particularly virulent bug that laid him low with meningitis soon after his return to this country. He spent nearly six months in hospital and on convalescence, before taking up the cudgels again in June 1981.

In the meantime, his highly-competent project team, led by Nigel Warner and Wade Holland, ensured that the tempo of the job did not slow down.

The work went on, and the fact that it all finished right on time and right on budget is a unique example of how easy it is for Clients, Architects, and Main Contractors to achieve miracles.

Only to get to that level, Client needs to be a professional jester, with no knowledge of, or interest in, Construction – but a master in the art of extortion; Architect must have an inexhaustible store of talent and energy – besides living on Client's doorstep; and main contractor's top man must also have a chain of national newspapers that will help find the money for it all.

After that it's all downhill!

Incidentally, the full title of that 'professional jester' is Doctor Jimmy Savile, Order of the British Empire, Knight Commander of Saint Gregory (*a Papal decoration*) Doctor at Laws!

The 'Olympians' who helped to create the new National Spinal Injuries Centre at Stoke Mandeville:

Client: The Jimmy Savile Stoke Mandeville Hospital Trust

Architects: The Fitzroy Robinson Partnership

Consulting Engineers: R. Travers Morgan & Partners

Quantity Surveyors: Wakeman Trower & Partners

Landscape Architects: Derek Lovejoy & Partners

– and as his duties were the means of introducing this chapter, we'd better include:

Clerk of Works: Gordon Hammond

PART FOUR

Hunting in the Dark

17

Marketing

The facing page is taken from the front cover of what I called, in my old firm, our 'Prestige Brochure'. Except for the name, address and the Company logo along the bottom, the picture and eight words shown are all that appeared. Inside were six pages saying how good we were at what we did, and how methodically we set about doing it. The usual stuff. No technical or sales blurb about our products, just a few pictures and production systems, together with photographs and captions of well-known buildings where we had been specified to supply our equipment. Places like London Airport, London Weekend Television, National Gallery.

When I saw the original picture hanging in the crowded window of a novelty shop on Broadway back in 1966, I bought it for a dollar and took it home. It was a 15" x 12" black-and-white fuzzy reproduction – possibly of some long-forgotten movie scene – but I inked a small caption under it – 'Our First Board Meeting' – put it in a frame, and hung it over my desk in the office. During the ensuing 15 years I must have moved office six or seven times, but that picture was never far away.

It attracted quite a lot of comment from visitors, especially first-timers, some of whom would peer at it closely and try to identify us with the characters shown. I was usually No. 3 from the left.

As selling a Company is the first stage of selling its product, simple eye-catching introductory literature is essential. That's how that ex-Broadway 'show-stopper' found its way on to the front cover of ours. The picture

"In the beginning . . .

. . . we relied on our charm!

may have been rough, but the cover itself was of laminated heavy art card and printed in four colours.

Our full catalogue consisted of about 100 A4 pages in a number of colour-coded brochures, describing the different things we made; but that prestige brochure was the only one to go out in any marketing exercise – with a covering letter inviting requests for the full catalogue set, in its free-standing ring binder.

It was amazing how many replies we had, asking if we could spare another copy or two of the introductory brochure, irrespective of whether a full catalogue was wanted or not!

An old 'Olympian' friend had a framed one, standing on a crowded shelf in his office. When asked why, he said it helped him cope with a bad day just to sit back and study it over his mid-morning coffee. It intrigued him how any firm claiming to be so good at what it did, would want to use a poor-quality picture of repulsive people to market its image.

But he confessed, despite the other manufacturers who worked on him for consideration when the next job came along, those four pairs of menacing eyes warned that, if he knew what was best, there was only one firm to think about seriously!

All that to introduce the subject of Marketing. It doesn't matter what you do or make, the finished product or service is usually comparable with that of a competitor. So what's left? Motor car manufacturers claim their model has a better shape, power, strength, safety or gimmickry than what their rivals offer for a similar price. In the fashion trade they boast of superior style or material. With furniture and furnishings it's colour combinations, durability, and ease of fixing. Those who want you to get smashed on their liquor, say that you'll wake up feeling less awful than if you'd done it on somebody else's embalming fluid. And so on.

But in Construction most of those sales or marketing features, where applicable, will be used in a watered-down form by 'Olympians' trying to get the design appointment. The only marketing 'tools' left to mortal 'hunters' are: usual characteristic claims to superiority, low cost, and some form of image in the eyes of the 'hunted-one' that might win favour.

'Characteristic claims to superiority' are those standard clichés used by hunters in any industry since time immemorial. Many will say they can be relied on to do a reliable job; or they take pride in finishing within the specified time; or their standard of work is guaranteed by their trade association; or they never claim for variations unless agreed to be just and fairly priced; or they have a proud reputation to uphold and would never do anything to sully it. There are many variations to the theme.

Have you ever known anybody claim to be unreliable, unpunctual, unfair, or sub-standard. Before the appointment, that is. After – well, the facts will speak for themselves. As they so often do – too late!

Trying to win a 'Hunt' on low cost alone is already covered in one or two of the earlier chapters. There are only two clear messages to pass on now. The first is for cost-crazy 'Olympians' to bear in mind.

It's just a quotation attributed to John Ruskin, an English author and essayist of the last century. As I've had difficulty in verifying it, the words may not be 100% accurate, but to the best of my memory it goes something like this:

There is nothing on this Earth that some man cannot make a little more cheaply; whomsoever buys on price alone is that man's lawful prey.

The second message is to the mortal 'Hunters' – to those who believe the only way to win is to be the cheapest in the field every time.

They would be well advised now to spend something from their dwindling coffers on a good stock of safety-matches, and to buy a pitch in the entrance to one of our busier main-line railway stations. For just as sure as God made little apples, that's where they're going to finish up!

Which brings us to what could well be the full title

"He was always the lowest bidder!"

of this chapter: [Marketing an image designed to win favoritism[.]

The preparation of this book involved a lot of research among those featured in the front line of Construction 'hunting'. Architects, quantity surveyors, engineers, and builders have all been visited and found to be extremely helpful. On the way out, I've sometimes asked for, and been given, a copy of their 'hunting' literature. This was always a well-designed four-colour brochure of anything between 12 and 50 pages, with photographs and descriptive matter concerning some of their more impressive projects.

The text and message throughout the brochure followed a similar theme in every case. Something like: 'Here are just a few examples of how our methods and experience have resulted in a fine-looking building. We have all the specialist staff and expertise to produce something equally unique for you.' They show photographs of key executives, grim-lipped with determination, anxious to get on with the said unique-production.

Almost every brochure had the hallmarks of being professionally designed by practitioners in advertising, as the J. Walter Thompsons and the Saatchi and Saatchis of this world like to designate themselves. With the result that they are beautiful examples of the professional approach to marketing material – individual in design, but equal in artistic merit; individual in style of presentation, but identical in their message. Yet the whole purpose of putting a name on a piece of marketing literature is to persuade the recipient that it's the only name to remember when the need arises.

If every side-show on a fairground banged a big drum, adding another drum with the same tempo will only increase the din, and do little to draw attention to a particular drummer. But if that drummer learned to stand up and play a trumpet instead, against that background of drums, he will not only be noticed more quickly, but will stay noticed. When the trumpet-player in a band starts up and plays the melody, how many eyes remain riveted on the bloke bashing the drums??

A Client receives scores of professionally put-together packages from would-be 'Olympians' and contractors. Even when there aren't 20 storeys of onyx in the offing! He can't stop the postman from delivering them, nor the 'hunters' leg-men or P.R.O.s from dropping them in – but it's doubtful if more than one in ten of those expensive presentations ever reach the 'big man's' desk, let alone get more than a cursory glance. As he puts the latest one into the 'Out' tray, destined for the catalogue library shelves – or more likely the waste-paper basket as the shelves are already bowing with the collected works of 'hunters' – he'll probably mutter something like, 'Not another! – See one you've seen 'em all!'.

All this might be considered negative criticism, but I'm afraid it's not easy to enlarge on a positive alternative approach. Not in the context of this book, anyway. So much depends on who's being 'hunted' by what kind of 'hunter'.

In the meantime, the only advice I can give to those wanting to put one over the other 'drummers' is – learn to play the trumpet!

With regard to 'hunters' among sub-contractors and manufacturers, marketing is a more straightforward matter. They don't have to pretend that they're not really trying to sell their wares or services. Nor do 'Olympians', come to that, although so many consider it unprofessional and vulgar to boast too openly of their skills.

But 'Jim'll Fix It' should be the battle-cry at the forefront of any 'hunt', even if there isn't a single Jim among the top team of the firm. (It doesn't sound the same if you put a Wally or a Charlie in there!) And that should also be the theme when selling the Company image with the help of its prestige literature.

When it comes to Sales, as opposed to Marketing literature, there's no reason why the two shouldn't be combined. Especially in the Construction industry. To differentiate between marketing and selling – the former is the process of creating a desire for a product or service; while selling is persuading the customer to part with his money and buy it from you. Sales literature is usually the catalogue of 'nuts and bolts'.

I'll finish the chapter with the closing lines from a magazine article I wrote early in 1985:

> Keep producing literature, but not thick expensive catalogues. In the first place, a strong free-standing binder, in which your informative paperwork can be retained – permanently.
>
> Then frequent distribution of single sheets describing, for instance: the latest addition to your range, changes or modifications to something you've already issued, an item or two of interest regarding your last big job, or even a description of the firm's beano to Brighton! It all keeps your name where it should be – in sight of your customer.
>
> He needs to get your binder down from his shelf each time to insert your latest communiqué. Or your rep will call in and do it for him. And every sheet issued should be emblazoned with the firm's name, etc.
>
> Remember what Geoffrey Chaucer said in 1374:
>
> *'He who whispers down a well*
> *About the goods he has to sell;*
> *Can never hope to make the dollars*
> *Like the man who stands on a tree and*
> *hollers!'*

Well, if it wasn't Chaucer I bet he wished he thought of it!

18

They Also 'Hunt' Who Only Want to Serve!

Although some reference has been made to manufacturers and suppliers being part of a 'Hunt', most of the book consists of describing people actually engaged in putting the building up. If the total price of a typical project were split into the cost of materials and that of labour, the latter would be around 40%. The other 60% would be spent on bought-in materials that need to be fixed under, on, around, above, and inside the structure. Within that percentage is, of course, the traditional mark-up by the various contractors for ordering, off-loading, inspecting, storing and paying for the goods, by which time they've cost Client quite a lot more than their original cost.

A manufacturer will often 'hunt' an 'Olympian' if his product is something of a speciality. Once all technical and financial factors are agreed, he'd have won himself one of the most-prized objectives of any manufacturer engaged in a 'Hunt' - that of a 'nominated supplier'. The price he has agreed with the relevant 'Olympian' will be written into the tender documents as a prime cost amount (P.C. sum). This means that those tendering for the site work involving that product need to include for buying it at the prime cost shown. What profit or handling charge they choose to add is up to them, but if they're tendering in tight competition they're not going to be too greedy. More likely they'll try to wheedle a bit of a token discount from the supplier who – if he feels a bit cocky in his nominated position – will say there's nothing doing. But even if a manufacturer does think he's got it made with his 'Olympian' friend, it pays to have a bit in hand to give back to the contractor who has to order and pay for it; often in the form of a credit note in case he has to produce invoices to Q.S. A co-operative contractor can be most helpful should queries arise over the quality or delivery of the goods he's been told to buy from a specific source. Also, that little 'give-back' can be geared to him paying the supplier quicker than he might have done otherwise.

Generally speaking, the bulk of bought-in wares that go to make up a building are ordered at the discretion of contractors, main and sub-, whose experience and friendships help them decide which of the various brands on offer they should favour. To encourage a favourable decision, stores personnel and purchasing managers of contracting firms are 'hunted' continuously by salesmen bearing samples, catalogues and order books, with a fund of free gifts and 'did you here the one about –?' Due to a limited expense account, hospitality when offered is limited to beer and a banger in the pub across the road.

But there's usually one big annual 'Hunt' by manufacturers to set the scene for the daily chase by their field staff. I refer to the Trade Exhibition. Or rather – Exhibitions, for there are literally scores of them. Some of those connected with Construction, and held in London or Birmingham during the first six months of the year, include Building and Construction; Cleaning and Maintenance; Contract Flooring; Estates and Property; Tiling; Office Environment; Fire and Security; Plant and Works; Elec. Installations and Contr.; Building Structure; Window; Electro-technical; Htg Vent. Air Con. and Bldg. Services; Power, Communications and Distribution.

That's only *some* of those held just in London and Birmingham. The *Exhibition Bulletin*, from where I took the above information, lists many more titles that could be associated with Construction, and many more cities and towns holding such exhibitions. In the classified section they list 37 exhibitions between October 1985 and

April 1987 held in this country under the heading of 'Building and Construction' alone. Not to mention 31 Electrical and Htg-and-Ventilation.

When planning exhibitions, conferences, shows, fairs, or any other fancy title that means pretty much the same thing, organisers try to make them sound as sweeping as possible, in order to tempt as many as they can into the net. Nervous and inexperienced manufacturers get scared they might miss out on the big chance by not being there – or be thought to have gone out of business – and can be conned into any number of local and national events by smooth-talking people selling exhibition space at trade shows.

Astronomical sums are spent on renting space, erecting stands, hiring furnishings, preparing displays, and generally trying to impress the hordes of eager-eyed V.I.P.s expected to come to call. At the back of the *Exhibition Bulletin* there are 137 headings under which the names of firms offering services to the would-be exhibitor are listed alphabetically. From Animated Displays and Artificial Grass – through Barrier Ropes, Drink Dispensers, Floral Decorators, Leaflet Holders, Muslin Ceilings, and Promotional Giveaways – on to Turntables, and finally Wallpaper. There are 30 pages to this directory section, and with about 30 names to a page, there must be something like 500 firms 'hunting' potential exhibitors, bearing in mind that some names appear under more than one heading.

Besides spending half an 'arm-and-a-leg' on his exhibition stand, our 'Hunt'-crazed manufacturer does the other half in rushing special exhibits through his drawing office and works – and new promotional literature to back them up through his printers. Then there's the key sales and technical staff, taken away from normal duties to wait on the anticipated hordes of visitors following up those expensive display advertisements in the trade press – announcing to all and sundry who you are, the number and location of your stand, and just what kind of wildly exciting things you plan to display.

Despite all that spending and publicity, comes opening day and you find every stand but yours has attracted attention. From your vantage point on one of the less costly sites in the gallery of the Hall, you look down on the milling throng in the central gangways below, and crowding the stands of your competitors. You then look at the sum total of your visitors that morning. An overseas student collecting as much literature as he can cram into an already-bulging briefcase, a passing elderly gentleman who asks if he can sit down on one of your chairs as his feet are killing him – and while doing so tells you it's almost time for his heart pill and could you oblige with something to help it down – like a little vodka-and-tonic, and a couple of blokes wearing exhibitors' badges in their lapels, killing a bit of time with a wander round the hall before returning to their own stand.

'It's a waste of time and money up here,' you reflect bitterly. 'Next time, if we ever survive the crippling cost of all this, we'll do it in style and get down there in the "big-time"!' Miraculously you survive, and spend half the national debt on a ground floor stand twice the size and three times the cost of the one you had previously. Comes the big event.

You listen to the public address triumphantly welcoming the two millionth visitor to pass through the turnstiles that day. You then look at the milling hordes on your own stand: seven multi-national students stuffing your literature into samsonite attaché cases; three apprentices in jeans and trainers sprawling on your hired upholstered chairs, the gentleman with the bad feet has a lady with him this time, who complains to your sales manager at the absence of tequila on the stand, two swarthy gentlemen laden with the literature from about every firm in the Hall and wanting your best price for 25,000 of your XB93's, and how soon can you get them on a boat for Jeddah if they come round with the letter of credit tomorrow morning (they never do), and three blokes from the architect's department of the Barchester Town Council, three-parts smashed on your booze, waiting for someone called Derek – or maybe Eric – because they'd arranged to meet him on your stand and he's an hour late already. Yours was chosen because the stand number, A147, has the same three digits as the number plate on Derek's (or Eric's) Toyota!

Visitors to exhibitions who might be in a position to feed through an order are few and far between. For what it's worth, here's some advice on how to get the worthwhile ones to visit your stand if you feel you've got to be there.

First get the stand-fitters to put down a well-carpeted floor and to provide a good-quality finish to the shell walls and fascias. Then have them put your trading name and logo in characteristic style, nice and bold and wherever possible, to ensure it can be seen from every direction. Have them build an inner four-sided enclosure almost as big as the floor with two doors – one at each end. Have them put you in a desk with a couple of phones, a large well-stocked bar, and as much comfortable seating and occasional tables as the rest of the space will allow. Leave all your exhibits, samples and catalogues 'back at the mill'! Staff the stand with a couple of your chattiest secretaries – not necessarily voluptious or 'chocolate-box' – and make up your mind it's going to be your personal H.Q. for the week, (you being the boss!). If you're too important 'back at the mill', or for some reason unapproachable, then get your second-in-command to do it. Have plenty of hard-binder memo books in which to record relevant data of the people you meet. (Record as much as possible at the time of the meeting, it's surprising how much gets forgotten for all time five minutes later in a carnival atmosphere.)

Ten days before the Exhibition is due to open, send a short personal letter of invitation to every influential individual you know, in every firm you know, and from whom an order or recommendation can do some good.

Also to those you only know of, but would like to know better. Split each day up into four two-hour periods, assuming the place is open from 10 to 6.0pm. Or 1½ hours if that works out better.

Go through your invitees and group them up into what you think will be a natural mix for party purposes. Allocate each group two or three of the periods staggered through the duration of the show. Then write the invitation explaining that you are making Stand No. XYZ your personal office throughout the exhibition, and, whereas they are most welcome to pop in and see you at any time if visiting the place, it would be rather nice if they could make it for one (or in fact all three) of the stated periods. Because that is when you've organised a little cocktail party, at which one or two people you feel they will be pleased to see will also be there. Probably.

It must be a personal letter, with just variations to the times and days. With modern word-processing type-writers (not like the one on which I'm banging out this literary masterpiece – a 35 year old portable smothered in Tippex stains) it should be a doddle.

With only a 20% acceptance, you'll at least have the right people coming to see you. And if they've enjoyed your company and that of some of the folk they met on your stand, a week or two later they will be pleased to say hello when you or your chosen delegate come to call and talk freely of what you want to sell – long after the tumult and the shouting at the Exhibition is over.

Once the sounds of merriment from your enclosure start echoing around the Hall, it's surprising how many visitors to the non-alcoholic marketing showpieces on other stands start directing envious glances and halting footsteps in the general direction of your 'hooley'. And, who knows, one or two of those might turn out to be useful.

I think it was Confucius who once said that anybody who likes a drink and a party can't be all bad. But remember to take lots of water with yours, because you're supposed to work very hard at being a good host!

Going back to what you need to hire: other than essential furnishings, I recommend a professional dog-handler – with a couple of Dobermann Pinschers – to keep those blasted students and apprentices off your pitch!

I go back more than 20 years, when the Electrical Engineers' Exhibition was held at Earls Court, London, every other year. For three successive exhibitions I went through all the traumas described earlier, taking a larger and more expensive stand each time. We did all the conventional things, like working through the night during the run-up period in order to get special exhibits and publicity literature ready in time, dreaming up ingenious display ideas, sending out chatty news-letters about what we were going to show, and taking half or full pages in the trade press to tell all and sundry the same thing.

After the show was over, and the euphoria and exhaustion worn off, all we were left with was a lorry-load of useless bits and pieces, and a lot of big bills. There were also the enquiry forms completed by visitors to the stand to be followed up, but they rarely came to anything. So few of those visitors had any authority to speak of when it came to it.

Then the penny dropped. When the next show was due to be held at Earls Court, I asked the Secretary of my Club, the Eccentric of St James's, if I could have the exclusive use of two meeting rooms on the second floor for that week. The Club was close to Green Park Station, which in turn is only a few stops on the Piccadilly Line from Earls Court. On the massive mahogany boardroom table occupying the centre of one of the rooms, we displayed samples of whatever specialist or interesting production items were going through the factory at the time. In the adjoining room was laid on a bar and a comprehensive hot-and-cold buffet, together with attendant liveried Club staff. The Club's best silver, glassware, crockery, and napery were provided for the use of my guests.

Selective invitations, similar to those suggested earlier, were sent to all our friends – including those from out of town that we thought might be coming to London for the Earls Court Show. It was suggested that perhaps they might like to come along, and bring their friends, to enjoy the ambience of a St James's Club after the wearisome walkabout at the Exhibition. Or come along at the suggested time even if they weren't going to Earls Court.

Club facilities, like bedrooms, bathrooms, barber shop, and billiards room, were made freely available to our guests. Any expense they incurred anywhere in the Club was to be put on the firm's account. We did it for four days, with two sessions per day. Twelve noon to 3pm and 4.30 to 7pm. I think the first session ran into the second once or twice, and seem to recollect the second session finishing around midnight. Especially on Friday, the final night! Those of us doing the hosting would take it in turn to grab a quick bed, shower, or a couple of hot-towels between sessions to recharge flagging 'batteries'!

The Club Committee, of which I happened to be a member at the time, liked the party atmosphere, not to mention the increased revenue from food, drink and use of the Club facilities, to the extent of circularising the membership and suggesting they consider running similar business seminars at the Club.

The total cost to my Company was the Club charges for food and drink, plus a healthy *pourboire* to the staff who helped make it such a success. And it was such a success that we repeated it two years later, and again two years after that!

The Exhibition changed its venue from London's Earls Court to the new National Exhibition Centre at Birmingham during the mid-1970s and that seemed a good time to call a halt to the biennial Morley Eccentric Show. It was a great success in public relations, and lasting goodwill sprang from those three four-day festivals. Nevertheless, having learned the hard way from those pre-Eccentric days, there was no anxiety to return to conventional exhibiting.

We did an annual Golf Day instead.

About 150 people, whether they golfed or not, were invited to come and spend a day at my golf club. Bring their ladies too, if they so wished. The Company's name and publicity material would be spread discreetly around the club lounge, and there would be enough Company staff and personal friends present to ensure everyone had a good day. This would be achieved with the help of a good choice of food for lunch and supper, assisted by a free bar.

Golf would be secondary, with the non-golfers being given partners from among those who could play well. Prizes, like power tools and things for the home, would not always go to the top-scorers – quite the reverse sometimes – but over ten years the day became an institution.

So much so that when I retired in 1982 I was prevailed upon to keep it going as an annual September event, with the cost of the day shared among those attending. Usually about 60 in number.

The last one was 1985, as the work on this book left little initiative to organize a Golf Day for 1986. And September 1987 is too far away to make any predictions for the future.

19

Epilogue

The purpose of this book was to present a light-hearted and irreverent survey of how business is pursued in Construction.

A fictitious large project has symbolised the objective of a 'Hunt', and most of the 'hunters' identified with people and firms well established in the upper ranks of the industry. Where I and/or my old business are brought into the story, the intention has been to illustrate a point from personal experience, rather than to show off or to attract attention. Mine was a small outfit compared to most of the giants that feature in these pages, but the 'hunting' procedures and opinions I describe are common to most of us. And, without quoting from my own memories, it would have been difficult to highlight some of the points needed to tell the story properly.

Grandiose projects, with eminent 'Olympians' and 'mortals' were used to illustrate how the linkages are formed, but, scaled up or down, the fundamentals are constant.

'What's he talking about now?' I hear from the back of the hall. Simple.

No matter how large the concept, one cannot draw more than one line at a time, lay more than one brick at a time, fix more than one switch at a time. It's just that the bigger the job, the more people engaged in drawing lines, laying bricks, fixing switches. The rules of Construction apply as equally to the lean and hungry self-employed Architect, bricklayer, electrician, or etcetera, as they do to the 'fat cats' of the industry.

But organised 'hunting' as described, with clearly defined 'lines-of-force' between 'Olympians' and the various levels of 'mortals', belong more to the larger commercial developments where they excel in spending other people's money – than to the smaller residential ones where Client is so often spending his own.

Having used the opening passages of the Bible to raise the curtain on my story, we can return to the same Book of Genesis for its finale. The Creation was paraphrased to illustrate the familiar site procedure of the First Construction Project. The following was partially taken from an old church magazine, modified a little, and now serves to illustrate the eternal progress-problems from another well-known Biblical Construction project, and how the 'First Client' solved them!

And the Lord said unto Noah: 'Where is the Ark which I have commanded thee to build?'

And Noah said unto the Lord: 'Verily the carpenter hath left the site due to non-arrival of gopher wood – yea, though the gopher wood hath been on order for nigh upon a twelvemonth. The damp-course specialist hath the ague. What can I do, O Lord?'

And God said unto Noah: 'I want an Ark finished even after seven days and seven nights'.

And Noah said: 'It will be so'. And it was not so.

And the Lord said unto Noah: 'What seemeth to be the trouble this time?'

And Noah said unto the Lord: 'Mine scaffolding erector is in liquidation. The pitch thou didst command me to put on the outside and inside of the Ark is in short supply and I'm having to buy it on the Black Market (Verily, O Lord, no joke is intended thereby). The plumber has withdrawn his labour claiming payment on his last certificate is overdue.'

And Noah rent his garments and said: 'The glazier hath departed on holiday to Egypt – yea, even though I did offer him acceleration bonus to complete on target. Shem, my son who helpeth me on the Ark side of the business, is on a 'go-slow' with his brothers, Ham and Japheth, for a share of the profits. Lord, I am undone!'

And Lo! it was not fulfilled.

And Noah then said unto the Lord: 'Verily, I now bring good tidings. The gopher-wood merchant hath had a delivery this day and but awaits the return of his servant from lunch before he despatcheth the gopher wood to site.'

And the Lord smiled upon Noah but then grew angry and said: 'What about the animals? Of fowls after their kind, and of every creeping thing of the Earth after his kind; two of every sort have I ordered to come unto thee to keep them alive. Where, for example, are the giraffes?'

And Noah said unto the Lord: 'They are promised for tomorrow morning without fail'.

And the Lord said unto Noah: 'And where are the clean beasts, the male and the female: to keep their seed alive upon the face of all the Earth?'

And Noah said: 'Scheduled for Tuesday's van. Yea and yea, it will be so'.

And the Lord said unto Noah: 'How about the unicorns?'

And Noah wrung his hands and wept, saying: 'Lord, Lord, they are a discontinued line. Thou canst not get unicorns for love nor money!'

And God said; 'Where are the monkeys, and the bears, and the hippopotami, and the elephants and the zebras and the hartebeests, two of each kind: and of the fowls also of the air by sevens, the male and the female?'

And Noah said unto the Lord: 'They should arrive by Friday; all save the fowls of the air by sevens, for it has been said that fowls of the air now come only in half-dozens.'

And Noah kissed the Earth and said: 'Lord, Lord, Thou knowest in Thy infinite wisdom what evil is wrought by contractors and suppliers and all Thy servants involved in all forms of Construction,

when it comes to fulfilling delivery and completion undertakings?'

And the Lord in his infinite wisdom sighed and said: 'Noah, My son, I knoweth full well. Why else dost thou think I prepare a mighty deluge to descend upon the Earth?'

There endeth the Final Lesson

——— 20 ———

Postscript

And there also endeth my word-picture of the Construction 'Hunt'. I've tried to keep it reasonably objective in a light-hearted way, although some of my opinions could be considered disparaging or irreverent. There's also the possibility that one or two 'brush-strokes' might appear slovenly or inaccurate to readers with more than a passing knowledge of a particular subject. But, as was said in the prologue, this is supposed to be an Impressionist 'picture' – based on impressions made on me by whatever I've seen, heard or read. There may well have been unknown factors likely to have changed them but, being unknown, they could not be expected to affect those impressions.

Where I've not drawn from my own experiences, information was sought from authoritative people and literature. It has involved much leaning against bars or sitting around lunch tables. That is why, at this postscript stage, I am now one-and-a-half inches more around the middle than when I started the prologue seven months ago. But the slog is over, and I hope to get the sylph-like shape back in time for publication revelries six months hence (I hope!)

I wanted to acknowledge all the help I've had in putting this story together, but many of those who provided it hold – or have held – important positions in business or Government circles. Some have said they'd rather not be openly associated with my descriptions or comments, in view of possible embarrassment at a later date. So, to follow Jimmy Savile's policy toward attending sponsored events during his appeal (see Chapter Sixteen) – if I can't name them all I shan't name any. (If and when it occurs I shall invite them all to the publication launch, the apprehensive ones hiding their identities behind false beards, dark glasses and hair-pieces!)

One who should be named, however, is Rodney Abbott, ex-editor of *Lighting Equipment News*. In the early days of 1985 he published an article I wrote for him on the lighter side of exporting. He then asked for another on the mysteries of getting specified in Construction. 'Only not more than a thousand words!' he warned, as the last one had run into about three times that number. In my first attempts to oblige, I linked the subject with the 'horse-opera' featured in Chapter Seven, but once past 4,000 words and still not a finish in sight, I realised it could well run to a possible book. That now being the case I'll take this opportunity to say, 'Sorry, Rodney, you never did get your 1,000 words, but I'm holding you partially to blame for what's taken its place!'

We now come to the man responsible for the drawings. Jo Varney, a past captain of South Herts Golf Club, is also an artist of great repute. He has done more than 4,000 cartoons for the *Daily Mail* over the past 15 years, and thousands more for national magazines and trade publications. He also contracted to provide two or three per week when Eddie Shah started his new high-tech *Today* at the beginning of 1986.

But serious art is his first love. He was commissioned by the Parachute Regiment to paint a full-sized portrait of Colonel H. Jones, V.C. their Commander-in-Chief, who was killed in action at the Falkland Islands. The finished work, beautifully executed in oils and from photographs, hangs in the officers' mess at the regimental H.Q. at Aldershot. Jo also volunteered to paint a portrait of the youngest member of the regiment killed in the same campaign; Jason Burt, aged 17½. For this too, he worked from photographs, and donated the finished work to the boy's parents.

I was quite proud when he agreed to do the drawings for this book. Especially as it meant him fitting them in between a heart by-pass operation, some busted ribs when he overturned in a golf-cart on a course near Boulogne, demands from his newspaper clients for the daily spate of cartoons, a children's book he was illustrating for a firm marketing watches, and a superb full-length portrait of the late Dai Rees, C.B.E. He finished the latter in a mad dash against the clock, but in time to be hung in the newly-built Dai Rees commemorative lounge at South Herts Golf Club when it was officially opened on Sunday 22nd June 1986.

● ● ●

Finally, a word of explanation to the cause of Feminism.

Wherever I may have used the word 'he', 'his', or 'him' throughout these pages, please feel free to read 'she', 'hers', or 'her'. Used in generic form, the feminine pronouns would apply equally well in most cases, but keeping to an all-male 'cast' has helped maintain a smooth descriptive flow.

It should be borne in mind, however, that although there is no shortage of the fair sex among Clients, Architects, or the Civil Service, there are not that many ladies in quantity surveying, engineering, or front-line Construction 'hunting'.

As for 'bricklayettes' or 'electriciesses', if they exist at all they must be thin on the ground, because I don't ever remember seeing any. At least, not on British ground – although I do remember elderly Chinese ladies, in shapeless black trouser-suits, carrying weighty buckets of wet cement up and down rickety ladders on Hong Kong building sites. But then, how many of them will ever get round to reading this!

"...build up with a half bucket of water, stir gently..."

—— APPENDIX A ——

Architectural Competitions

A Client with an impressive project in mind, but feeling he'd like a wider choice of original artistry than that available from a single practice, might decide to go in search of it by way of an Architectural Competition. This could also be the means of some nice publicity for Client as a patron of the arts – perhaps even pave the way to a Birthday or New Years Honours listing!

The Royal Institute of British Architects, hereafter referred to as R.I.B.A., issue a handbook consisting of 65 foolscap pages on the subject. It lays down the conditions and guidelines of the different kinds of competitions, and caters for student exercises, scholarships, small and large commercial developments, and grand Government schemes for building the nation's landmarks. A commercial development such as P.A.G.'s could be competed for in four different ways:

1. In a Preliminary Project Competition, a limited number of Architectural practices will be given some outline information on the proposed project and asked to submit details of experience in similar work, also to give some indication how they would set about this one. R.I.B.A. would provide a panel of four experienced architects who would help Client prepare the project Brief, and act as the Assessment Panel when judging the returns. They would set questionnaires so that answers could be evaluated competitively. (Not much different to contractors tendering for a job and, although there's no mention of it in the handbook, I bet the candidate's proposed fee and disbursement

structure is something that Client will want to know about!)

But according to the book it's the Assessment Panel who decide which of the competitors they consider most suitable for the appointment, and the remainder get an agreed *ex gratia* payment from Client for their troubles. If building is not started within six months of his selection, the winner is entitled to Scale fees as laid down by R.I.B.A.; but if he hasn't received instructions after 12 months the competition is ended and Client has to pay everybody whatever is written into his contract with R.I.B.A.

2. In a Single-Stage Project Competition, the panel assist Client to prepare a comprehensive project Brief and an advertisement for architectural circles inviting suitable applicants to take part in the 'Hunt'. These are short-listed to an agreed reasonable number to whom the brief-package is then sent. It will consist of rules and conditions of the Competition, closing date, question-naires, and a detailed description of what Client is looking for. The Panel select the best three for Client to decide.

   The winning design is awarded first prize with the appointment to build, but his prize money is offset against his architectural fees once he starts to earn them. The other two get awards to the scale featured in the handbook, and there may be further *ex gratia* awards to other competitors.

3. A Limited Competition is similar to (2) except that just six or seven practices are invited to compete. These would be well-known for their exceptional skills in the specialised nature of the project envisaged by Client, or may have been pre-selected on a similar basis from a miscellaneous number answering an advertisement.

4. A Two-Stage Competition is similar to (2), except that in the first instance only a general description of pro-posals, backed up by simple line drawings, is asked of the competitors. From these the field is reduced to

something between six and ten, who are then invited to develop their designs. The winner's award is set against the fees he will earn from the project in the usual way, and all the remainder making the second stage will get something for their troubles.

Awards are on a sliding scale dependent on the value of the project, but *ex gratia* payments – or 'honoraria' as they are elegantly described by R.I.B.A. in the handbook – are dependent on the benevolence of Client and pressures exerted by R.I.B.A., the latter advising Client on type of Competition they recommend as being best suited to his needs.

Competitors would submit their entries by the stipulated date, with no indication of identity on drawings, specifications, and detail to be read in conjunction with drawings. They will all be delivered in plain envelopes or packaging, and in a separate plain envelope will be the completed questionnaire, together with any other information of a relevant nature concerning the competitor. Each set would be marked up with a registration letter or number, but the envelope containing the identity of the entrant would not be opened until the winning design has been selected.

Client is obliged to contract with R.I.B.A. that he will instruct the winner to commence the building programme within 12 months, but it may turn out that the winner, although strong on design, is not readily acceptable by Client because of doubt about his experience or resources. Should that situation arise, R.I.B.A. and its Assessment. Panel will undertake to find an established firm of architects with which the winner will collaborate throughout the job. This will be done on a shared-fee basis at no extra expense to Client. But, according to their model conditions, R.I.B.A. have the final word in any dispute over the running of the Competition or matters resulting therefrom

Having browsed through those model conditions at length, I doubt if R.I.B.A. today could persuade the average hard-nosed Client to accept them without question – carefully and heavily weighted as they are in favour of the organising body and its members. Assuming the project, excluding fees and land, is going to cost about £20 million, then the Scale awards and remunerations laid down for his Competition will cost Client as follows:

Awarded to winner in Comp. 2, 3, or 4	£14,000
Award to Second	7,000
Award to Third	4,700
Awards to remaining four competitors, say,	8,000
Four Adjudicators split 60% of First Award	8,400
R.I.B.A. Service Charge 20% of First Award	2,800

Other charges include fees to specialist advisers that the Assessment Panel deem necessary to engage in the preparation of the Brief, and re-imbursement of out-of pocket expenses to all and sundry in connection with travel, hotels, printing, advertising, exhibition and similar charges.

In all fairness I should explain that the formula on which the above awards and charges are calculated is based on a project costing not more than £5 million. The handbook states that larger jobs would be subject to negotiation. But even if there were a 20% reduction to the figures shown, Client's not going to get much change out of £40,000 at the end of his Competition.

For that sort of money a purposeful Client should want a lot more say than the conditions appear to allow him. But everything is under the absolute control of R.I.B.A., who advise their profession in the opening pages against entering Architectural Competitions except under the model rules they lay down in the handbook.

In these highly mercenary days, a shrewd Client would not be acting unreasonably if he told R.I.B.A. that 'he who pays the piper ought to have more say in calling the tune'. He'd want to adopt a more business-like approach to it all, bending R.I.B.A.'s conditions as necessary to conform with his views on the subject. He'd probably approach them with something along these lines:

I have a commercial site in a prime position, on which I want somebody to design a really imaginative building for me. Here's a scale plan of the site, prepared by my staff architect, with some other relevant details that he tells me might help you initially in putting the thing together. My needs are a large reception area at street level, onyx façade, parking for executive cars and V.I.P. visitors, lavish board-room and director suites, and so-many thousand square feet of high-tech. office space, all built with an overall magnificence that will not only enhance my own Company's image, but put the building's designer in among the front-runners of Who's Who in modern architecture.

Will you kindly recommend six reputable practices you think capable of handling this and willing to prepare preliminary designs and approximate budget costs. In those costs they must include not only their own fees, but those of any surveyors and engineers they may need to help them with their technical knowledge and skills throughout the duration of the project itself. In other words, I want an idea of what a design team is going to cost me before I appoint them, much the same as a contractor will have to submit a competitive price if he wants the job of building my masterpiece. But don't get me wrong, I'm not looking for the lowest bidder. Just a top-class design with no arguments later about design fees or expenses not included in the original budget figures.

Will you also please organise an Assessment Panel of four wise men, to work with me in preparing and marking the 'examination papers'. I shall rely throughout on their expertise and guidance, but the final decision in all matters must be mine. After the preliminary returns we will reduce the six candidates to two, and the four rejects will each get, say, £2,000.

The remaining two will then enter the second stage of the contest and present their schemes in detail, for which they will each receive, say, £5,000. The one declared the winner will be expected to set off his prize-money against fees earned when we start to build.

Yes, I undertake to start to build to the winner's design within twelve months from the closing date, with the following provisos:

1. If business conditions make it necessary to abandon the scheme, I shall pay the winner the difference between his award and the fee laid down in your rules for an abandoned project.

2. If nobody submits what I consider to be an acceptable design at the end of Stage One, they will all receive the same stage one payment and the contest will be called off. I then reserve the right to use the Competition Brief as I see fit in such negotiations as I may enter into with another designer.

3. Although I shall be playing a part in judging the winning design, I shall not know its author until after the decision is reached. In the unlikely event that my Company does not wish to be involved with that particular practice – for reasons that may have developed after they were first invited to compete – I reserve the right to use the Competition Brief in making fresh plans with another designer. I shall, of course, fulfil all my obligations under the terms of the competition.

With all this information now before you, will you, the Royal Institute of British Architects, quote me in detail for organising the whole thing. I shall want you to take care of all payments, both known and anticipated, and with this in mind shall need a priced Bill, covering anticipated variations and options, with your estimate. Once I get it we can meet again and agree what we do, what we leave out, and sign some papers. I'll put 50% of the bottom line up front, and you'll get the other 50% the day we declare the winner.

But if you anticipate any claims for travelling, hotels, telephone calls, displays, headache tablets, and all that jazz, you'd better have them agreed with me in that original Bill and estimate. Unless, of course, we've agreed it subsequently, and in writing!

The R.I.B.A. would probably insist on a few conditions to safeguard the interests of their members before agreeing to help in organising such a competition. Many large practices have special non-productive design sections where promising young people are encouraged to take part in such competitions. Should they succeed in winning one they'd be promoted to head the section of the practice responsible for creating the building.

But competitions are funny things and apt to get out of hand. They tend to become theoretical exercises for the budding *Bader-Meinhoffs* of the architectural profession. Having taken half-a-year to produce a carefully aimed 'spit-in-the-eye' at the 'proles' of convention and tradition, they enjoy the public furore so created. They then get all bewildered and wild-eyed if ever taken seriously and asked to go ahead with their revolutionary scheme. But more often than not the schemes are never implemented. Somewhere, somehow, a note of sanity creeps in.

The National Gallery is a case in point. Designed in 1833 by William Wilkins, its much-loved façade has graced the north side of Trafalgar Square for a century-and-a-half. Needs arose for an extension and the Trustees declared an open competition for a suitable design.

The entries from 'mods and rockers' of the architectural world appeared to have had one common theme. It simply told us, the lay public with established affection for grace and symmetry, to 'Get stuffed!'.

The declared winning design, when put on show, was beautifully summed up by our so-articulate Prince of Wales as: 'A monstrous carbuncle on the face of a much-loved and elegant friend!'. I don't believe anybody could have pronounced a more justified and damning criticism in so few well-chosen words. They brought about a public enquiry and the design was rejected. The competition became null and void.

It looked for a time that the whole idea of the much-needed extension would be shelved indefinitely. In all fairness, it should be explained that the competition was based on developers wanting a composite building, with viewing galleries on the lower levels and prime office space available for letting on the upper floors. Thereby the cost to the public for the museum part of the new building would be minimised. But not an easy building for an architect to blend harmoniously on to the end of a noble, 150-year old temple of art!

Around the middle of 1985, the Chairman of the National Gallery Trustees resigned. He is said to have played a big part in the decision to go out to competition, and in the decision when it came to choosing the winner. His place was taken by 'a Daniel come to justice', as Shakespeare might have said. Well not exactly a Daniel, but a Rothschild. Jacob Rothschild, to be precise.

Then, in gratitude to a nation's patronage of their grocery empire over the best part of a century, the Sainsbury family made a most magnificent gesture. They would pay for the design and development of a National Gallery extension, to match the existing building, from their own personal coffers. It would not cost the public a penny and there would be no need to house commerce in the same structure. Other, perhaps, than the inevitable souvenir shop, bookstall, and fast-food bar. All they wanted in return was an invitation to play a positive part in its design.

So there it is – a sound and practical business approach to a question of just what trained artists should provide to please the untrained eye of the discerning public. At this time of writing, January 1986, the main positive decision is that there are certainly not going to be any more competitions. A small group of investigators, comprising a couple of Trustees, the Sainsbury brothers, and the architectural expert from the *Financial Times*, are junketing around the world on a detailed study of new museums and the work of certain short-listed architects; four English and two American, all of whom, I understand, have been responsible for a number of impressive buildings on an international scale.

Once the group return and have lost both their tropical tan and jet-lag, they will present their findings to the Trustees. When these are analysed one of the six will be given a brief to build the National Gallery extension to a design that will meet with the approval of Client. And it's my opinion that the Client-'throne' will be a four-seater capable of taking Jacob Rothschild and the three Sainsbury brothers.

No more competitions, no more public enquiries, and – without a doubt – no more carbuncles!

—— APPENDIX B ——

Management Contracting

In the early 1960s a man called Sir Harold Emmerson was asked by the Ministry of Works, as the D. of E. was known then, to find out what was wrong with the Construction industry. In his report he expressed the view that, 'In no other industry is the responsibility for design so far removed from the responsibility for production'. As a result of that report, the Banwell Committee was formed about a year later to take the matter further. It recommended changes in contractual procedure aimed at bridging the gap between 'Olympians' and their erstwhile 'subjects'. It said that not only would Clients benefit from these changes, but all interested parties would be better informed from the outset and thereby benefit accordingly. It went on to recommend that certain types of large projects would best be served by a Project Management Team, in which the Builder would be an integral part of the design group, and that this would need a different approach to his appointment and payment than was the case with Traditional contracts.

There are a number of different formats for Project Management, but they all have one thing in common – the builder gets up on 'Olympus' as part of the design team and is in direct contact with Client. The three most common forms are Management Fee, Contract Management, and Design Management. Their distinctive features are as follows:

1. In Management Fee, the builder has a separate section, or company, in his organisation that specialises in management. It takes control of the complete project, which

includes monitoring the other 'Olympians', for a fixed fee.

It will appoint its own Project Manager who will sit on Client's right hand from the concept stage, and ensure that Architect's and Engineer's designs are easily interpreted by the people who have to work to them. Between them they will split the job into 'work packages'.

The Project Manager will get his own parent company to bid, in competition, for those packages that interest them. He will be responsible for all tender documents, place all orders, and supervise execution through to completion. For this he will charge Client the fixed fee quoted – not a percentage – and not deviate from it unless the nature of the job deviates considerably from the original concept.

That is the general principles of Management Fee, although different firms and different Clients finish up agreeing to any number of variations to the basic idea.

Some of the many advantages claimed by its supporters over the Traditional methods of contracting include:

a) With the first work-package let – say, site-enclosure or demolition – work can commence on site while the next package – say, excavation – is still being calculated prior to tender and ordering. This, of course, makes for a faster programme. From site-enclosure to floor-polishing, there could be up to 100 such packages on a large high-tech project.

b) By letting these packages near the time they are to be carried out, a fixed price can be obtained to the exclusion of rise-and-fall clauses. These latter are written into most traditional contracts, where prices are quoted as applicable to the month of tendering only, or a particular date specified in the documents, and then subject to a labour-and-material fluctuating cost index published monthly by Government statisticians.

2. In Contract Management, once again, the builder's appointed Project Manager is brought into the design team, to act in Client's best interests as Manager of Construction. But, instead of handling the tendering and letting of work-packages, although still part of the team that prepare them, he would be responsible for site performance and progress only. Client, usually through Q.S., employs the package-contractors.

When 'hunting' the appointment, the potential Contract Manager will be asked to define and quote his price for providing plant, management staff, and site accommodation for all, throughout the duration of the project – together with his fee for management services quoted as a percentage of the total cost of the finished job. The figures he provides will be compared against those of other 'hunters' – and the best man wins.

All site discipline comes under his control, and he is in uninterrupted contact with Client at all times. Contractors' interim and final accounts need to be cleared by him before being passed for Client and Q.S. to deal with.

One important difference between Fee and Contract Management, is that, in the former instance, packages can be let to the parent company, or its subsidiaries, if the price is right. No firm remotely associated with the management team is normally allowed to tender for any part of a Contract Management project, where the fee is a percentage of the whole.

Every job is different, however, and as those concerned learn more about the advantages and problems of Management, they adapt its principles to suit each fresh situation.

There is also confusion caused by ambiguity of descriptive terms. An in-depth study is needed for a new vocabulary and a concise set of guidelines on terminology.

Since the start of Management projects only a few years ago, there have been signs of old habits creeping back. Shouldering the financial and practical burdens of a site was one of the usual crosses borne by a main contractor in traditional jobs. Although now in the design team, the Contract manager springs from main-contractor stock, and is 'passed the buck' when the situation arises by those long experienced in playing that game, despite the fact that he's only there to use his know-how and experience in getting Client a fast, trouble-free job at an economic price. But quantity surveyors, who usually draft the contracts, are building financial obligations into Management terms that should be Client's responsibility. Managers are being conned into carrying the can for:

(1) Delays and expense incurred in the event of a work-package contractor going bankrupt before completing his job.

(2) Liquidated damages if a contractor is proved to have caused the job to over-run and fails to pay up.

(3) Repairs, replacements, or maintenance costs if a contractor fails to honour his obligations to take care of them

(4) Unforeseen flaws in design – it being claimed that, as the practical member of the design team, he should have brought them to light before they involved expense and delay.

With more and more builders setting up Management divisions, Clients have a seller's market, and can bully them into risk areas not covered by the tight margins necessary to succeed in the 'Hunt'.

The foregoing observations, with the blame squarely laid on the Q.S. fraternity, were harvested from an article in December 1985's *Chartered Quantity Surveyor*, by Ross Hayes, a well-known authority on Construction and Civil Engineering at Manchester University.

3. In Design Management, Client puts all his eggs into the basket of the Project Manager. Client has a concept for a development and may ask his in-house architect

to outline his needs. Or he may employ an independent design team to do it. He offers this skeleton brief to 'hunters' in the Management field, who compete with each other in presenting a comprehensive design-and-management package.

The winner has, or hires, his own design team to plan the job in detail from the outline designs provided by Client. He works throughout in close conjunction with Client and takes charge of the whole project. Working for the Management Company, the design team split the job up into the usual work-packages. These are discussed by Project Manager, with Client and his Q.S. or adviser, before being tendered for and let in the manner described.

Once again there are many variations to how this system of Management has been interpreted, depending on what sort of give-and-take is agreed between Client and Project Managers. But in Design Management, both Architect and Engineers, though rarely Q.S., all work for the erstwhile-builder. A complete reversal of traditional authority!

To sum up, in Management projects the builder is elevated to equal, if not superior, status of the traditional design team.

Architects and engineers, so long accustomed to the rarefied air and autocracy of the upper slopes of 'Olympus' – and at the foot of which they have been so used to seeing mortal hordes clamouring for their favours – don't enjoy taking orders or being monitored by some of those self-same mortals. Nevertheless, they all like to eat. And if finding the wherewithal for their daily intake means swearing allegiance to an ex-forelock-tugging builder, then down they plop on one knee and take the demanded oath of fealty, while sadly and silently bemoaning the passing of those bygone halcyon days, when servants knew their rightful place and beer was five pence a pint!

By the same token, specialist contractors and suppliers – so used to pursuing favours from Traditional 'Olympians' – find that no matter how cosy the old associations may have been, there's now a Project Manager and his team to be wooed and won if they're looking for a share of the spoils in a 'Hunt'!

—— APPENDIX C ——

'Pack-hunting!'

So far we've studied the 'hunting' field with every
contractor, sub-contractor and supplier doing his own
thing, and pursuing the 'Olympian' deity of his choice in
the manner he knows best. But in the long run – and the
'hunt' for a large prestigious project can be a very long
run – he's on a good hiding to nothing. Or very nearly
nothing.

To ensure the lowest possible figure is reached, there
could be a dozen or more invited to compete with each
other. All but one will be unsuccessful. And it's well on
the cards that the winner will either have made a costly
mistake, or have cut his prices well into the bone in order
to win the day. As a result nobody really benefits but
Client, who obviously gets his job done at a lower-than-
fair price. Quite often the others are not even told they
have failed. The first they learn of it is when they enquire
if a decision has been reached, only to be told that it has
and better luck next time.

So why bother to chase in the first place? Well, it's the
instinct of the born hunter. Even when no longer hungry
for the work, contractors and suppliers like to keep their
hand in at courting 'Olympians', as there's no knowing
when they'll be looking for favours on a future project.
And if lucky enough to win this one, there's always the
chance of one or two lucrative extras to boost the margins.
But the fact remains that winning first prize in a competitive bid involves a lot of cheeseparing and, to mix a
metaphor, the winner will need all the lucky windfalls he
can get unless he's out to lose money deliberately.

Little wonder, then, that at one time there was no small measure of collusion between groups of sub-contracting 'hunters'. Strictly illegal, of course, but quite understandable when you consider that they each had an expensive estimating department to run – with odds of anything up to 15-to-1 against recovering its costs, depending on how they were invited to tender for each job.

(I say 'at one time' for the simple reason that – as far as I know – 'Pack-hunting' belongs to the bad old days. The law is a lot stricter now, and I am told that sub contractors and suppliers of integrity will no longer risk indictment for fraud or bribery when searching for today's business. Having made that point there follows one or two examples of how some of yesterday's sub-contracting buccaneers set about their skullduggery. But it should be borne in mind that none of the firms or people featured elsewhere in this book are in any way associated with those described in the ensuing examples.)

In the bad old days, a 'pack-hunt' would start when a sub-contractor first learned that he had won his way on to a tender list. His initial reaction would be to get to know who was on the list with him. That was not always easy to learn but an enterprising 'hunter' would have one or two subtle ways of finding out. Once he had all the names he'd sound out his opposite number in each of the firms in turn, to see if they fancied a little secret 'summit' meeting.

Let us assume that eight firms were invited to tender for a £2 million sub-contract on a new construction project. On a job of that size it was possible for each of the eight to tie up four estimating engineers for a month, plus assistants and clerical staff, on what would prove to be both an expensive and abortive exercise for seven of them. But if all eight agreed to work as a team nobody was going to be out of pocket. But all eight had to agree. If just one of them didn't want to play, preferring to take his chance with a legitimate tender, then there could be no 'fix'. They would each have to go it alone – as, of course, they were supposed to do.

With 100% agreement the eight then became a newly-formed secret society. It had to be very secret. If the slightest whisper leaked out, disqualification would automatically follow with possible charges of attempted fraud.

Their first meeting was probably held in a private room of some out-of-the-way hotel. Once together they would discuss the nature of the job and how much information they were to provide when submitting their bids. That would decide them on how to go about planning the 'fix'. Several methods were used but I'll explain one or two:

1. On the basis that all were anxious to win the job, they would each agree to put their estimating departments to work and prepare a bona fide set of figures. Once ready, they would meet again a few days before the tenders were due in, and each produce his workings and bottom line. The eight totals would then be added together, and divided by eight. The one whose price was nearest to that figure was declared the winner. It obviously would not have been the lowest. Or the second lowest. So the winner already had a better margin than might otherwise have been the case.

   But he did not put his original price in. Nor the calculated one. For a job worth about £2 million he probably needed to add about 5% to the agreed figure, whereby he could pay the other seven about £5,000 each for their time and trouble. This they would have covered by issuing him with a series of invoices for the fictitious loan of labour to one of his jobs – not necessarily the one in question – or for supplying him with plant or materials. The pay-off was thus lost among the hundreds of legitimate accounts entered in the books of each of the conspirators.

   To complete the exercise of hoodwinking the 'Olympians', the assembly would have agreed what price they each put in over and above the 'manufactured' winner, taking care to adjust their cost-books accordingly when returning to base and before sending off their tenders. It would not have been unusual for Q.S. to ask one or two of the other tenderers – not just the one with the lowest bid – to produce a breakdown of how he arrived at his quoted figure, and all had to be ready for such a request.

2. To explain another method, we'll assume that when invited to tender one of the eight didn't want the job anyway. His estimators were busy on other work – or if he did win the 'fix', too many of his key personnel would be tied up on this project when he needed them badly elsewhere. Yet he'd be loath to send back the documents and ask to be excused from quoting in that particular instance. To have done that would have been bad for future business. 'Olympians' have long memories and, once given the 'elbow', would not be too keen on courting another refusal. Once having carefully prepared a list of proposed tenderers and had it approved by Client and/or Architect, a consulting engineer would feel he had lost face if his attempt to bestow grace and favour on a 'hunter' was rejected.

At the initial meeting of the newly-formed 'mafia' it was discovered, say, that two out of the eight, for varying reasons, did not want the hard slog of calculating a competitive price. It would not then have been fair for the remaining six to do so, as set out in the first section, knowing that five of them would get the same reward for an abortive effort as the two who didn't even try.

They'd consider alternative ways of deciding on a winner. One of the six may have been extra keen on the job and managed to persuade the others to stand down and let him have it. Or they decided that it was his turn anyway because he lost out on the last three 'fixes'. Or agreed just to spin coins, deal the cards, or draw lots.

Whatever the means of selection, the decision on

who was to have the job would be made at that first meeting. The winner would then have gone ahead to put in a handsome non-competitive figure, included in which, of course, would be the usual handout to his seven friends.

In exchange he was obliged to prepare seven additional sets of detailed calculations, all varying to a degree, for the others to enter up before sending in their manufactured higher prices.

3. Sometimes a tender would be based on a priced bill of quantities. That was a tedious task to fix. There could easily be several hundred items, each of which had to be individually priced and extended. To be awarded the contract a tenderer would need to present the lowest total for the specified items in the bill.

   When the 'fixers' got together and appointed their winner he would need to take care, when preparing the prices for the other seven, that he was not the lowest for every item. That would have aroused suspicion. He just needed to be low enough overall – winning a few, losing some – to ensure a clear-cut victory.

   It was done on a permutation basis. Sheets of paper were ruled up in the winner's estimating office, with the item numbers from the bills of quantity set vertically down the left-hand side of the page, and eight columns headed A to H. Contractor A, the winner, would go right through the job, putting the calculated figures from his cost book against each item in column A. He'd then adjust each of those figures by varying amounts and fill in the remaining seven columns; ensuring that his was the lowest on the dearer items but not when it came to some of the cheaper ones.

   He would take care that he wasn't always the best in the sub-totals at the bottom of each page, but also ensure there was no doubt whose figures were the most competitive when it came to the final figure.

   Once all had been thoroughly checked, a photostat

set of bills would be priced up from column B and passed to contractor B, to enter up in his cost book. Column C would be transferred to another set of photostats and sent to contractor C – and so on. With the exception of contractor A nobody would have known how his figures compared with the other seven.

Sometimes it would take just a bit more initiative and devilish cunning to get it all to work. This one I call 'The Sting'!

There was one large project many years ago where contractor A won the 'raffle', and had to fix the bills of quantity as described under item 3. But the consulting engineer, for personal reasons, was anxious for nobody but contractor B to have the job.

When the bids were opened on 'Olympus', he took copies of the tenders back to his office, ostensibly for checking. He then sent Client's staff engineer limited extracts from the rigged bills, where B could be seen to be cheaper than A. He explained in his covering letter that in view of certain agreed changes to 'Olympian' design, not catered for in the original bills, there would be considerable increases to quantities shown for those items once the job started. B had submitted lower prices for those items and, based on the increased quantities, consultant had done comparative calculations. They worked out to show B significantly lower than A, and therefore he recommended the order be placed with B.

Now what he did not know was that Client's staff engineer was just as anxious for contractor A to have the job. For personal reasons, of course. When he told A of this latest development they put their heads together to decide how best to deal with consultant's anxiety to sabotage their cosy relationship. It was done by staff engineer (S.E.) writing to consulting engineer (C.E.) explaining that C.E.'s efforts and research were much appreciated, but his recommendations could not be accepted. As eight leading sub-contracting firms had been asked to submit prices for supplying and fixing specific quantities of specific materials, it would not be ethical to award the prize to B because of possible new developments. At least, not without giving all eight the opportunity to re-quote on a similar basis. And as the target date was a tight one, there just wasn't time to do that.

In any case, he went on, being Client's man, he knew of further changes in the offing but not yet passed around on 'Olympus' for detailed design, and, on checking the approximate difference they might make to the original quantities, he found contractor A would still finish up the lowest.

C.E. told contractor B that any further effort would be in vain unless B set about winning the warmth and friendship of Client's S.E. There was no time to waste. And although B was present at that undercover meeting when it was decided that A should have the job, he couldn't say as much. He had to appear at least as eager to get it as C.E. was for him to have it! Anyway, with a job of that size in the offing and with an 'Olympian' working hard to help him get it, B had no trouble with his conscience when deciding to dishonour his obligations to A and go all out for the big prize himself.

His firm were renowned for the pleasantries they could provide when the needs arose. Client's staff engineer was invited to spend a long weekend, at B's expense, at a luxurious bungalow on a picturesque and panoramic reach of the Thames some way above Maidenhead. Having rented it especially for that purpose, B proceeded to stock the larder with the finest of food and wines from Harrods, and arranged for a sleek motor cruiser to be tethered on the water's edge at the bottom of the lawn. And to ensure the pampered guest would not get too lonely during those two long days and three short nights of that weekend, two nubile wenches were hired to share them with him!

Client's staff engineer was equally renowned for being fond of that sort of thing, and wasted little time in accepting B's magnificent gesture. But before leaving the office on Friday afternoon to go wallow in all that hedonistic luxury provided by contractor B – and in case he arrived back at the office on Monday a little too late and over-tired to deal with important matters – he had the order made out to contractor A and posted it himself as he drove out to Maidenhead. On the grounds that he was covered for a lot more than just a dirty weekend up the river if contractor A got the job!

Having written all that I thought was necessary on the subject, another classic comes to mind and is worth a mention in this section of the book.

Five or six contractors got together and fixed a 'fix' in one of the ways already described. It was to be a pre-arranged winner who had already come to terms with Client's staff engineer in charge of the project. The work involved quite a lot of refurbishment on each floor of a large existing building.

The job was completed and all authorised payments made to the sub-contractor involved, when a team of independent auditors arrived on the scene to check that the money had been spent wisely. Clients do this from time to time without warning, and occasionally come across strange goings on.

In this instance they found that not only had the sub-contractor set out in detail the work carried out on each floor and the price thereof – but his invoice charged for one more floor than there was in the building. And Client's staff engineer had authorised payment!

As I said in the fifth paragraph of this Appendix, all the stories told relate to a bygone era; an era that ended when the Office of Fair Trading carried out an in-depth investigation of reported bribery and collusion among sub-contractors in the industry. As a result draconian rulings and penalties were introduced, aimed at deterring all but the most foolhardy at drawing a bow at that kind of venture today.

Finally, the stories related are such as were told to me during those gregarious days among the fleshpots of clubs and bars. My own personal experiences in the matter are nil, as I traded at a level far below that at which one could qualify for membership of a 'Pack'!

—— APPENDIX D ——

The Clerk of Works

It was shown in Part Three that, whereas Clients often make good 'fiddlers', their practical knowledge of Construction is usually poor. Despite some self-important attempts to pretend otherwise. They are usually blind to the practical techniques and finer points of what goes into a finished job – and just as a blind person will use a trained guide-dog to take him safely along unfamiliar ways, a Client will use a trained 'watch-dog' to safeguard his interests throughout a Construction programme.

That 'watch-dog' is the Clerk of Works (or C. of W.). And just as no blind man would be safe if he ever tried to use more than one guide-dog to lead him around at any one time, a building site would be bedlam with more than one 'watch-dog' monitoring it. That is why Frank Cherry and his colourful observation was used, in Chapter Seventeen, to introduce the only man on a building site, from start to finish, who is completely independent of the design team and contractors. Although he does, in fact, normally report to Architect.

To use the official definition of his Institute, 'The Clerk of Works is an inspector, or superintendent, appointed by the owner of a building to see the work is carried out by contractors in accordance with the drawings and specifications produced by the Architect, and the bills of quantity drawn up by the Quantity Surveyor'.

The title originates from the medieval monasteries, where the monks were all Clerks in Holy Orders. The monk responsible for all building work was known as The Clerk of the Works. Geoffrey Chaucer, author of *The*

Canterbury Tales – and, allegedly, of the immortal words credited to him at the end of Chapter Seventeen of *Victory in Site!* – was appointed Clerk of the King's Works in 1389. But reading through his background in my reference books, he doesn't seem to have had the practical experience a latter-day C. of W. would need for the job.

Usually a mature ex-tradesman at supervisory level, like a foreman carpenter or bricklayer, he would have had to pass the exams laid down by the Institute of Clerks of Works Great Britain Inc. to claim qualification as a certified C. of W. And just as the blind man's guide-dog cannot approve movement, but quickly checks it when he does not approve, the same applies to a C. of W. on a building site. Only Architect has the authority to approve work done on site, but the C. of W. wastes little time in halting anything that doesn't meet his approval. And if Contractor chooses to contest the opinion instead of getting on with the necessary remedial action, it's odds-on that he'll get short shrift from Architect if he wants C. of W.'s decision reversed.

Their Institute, which is over 100 years old, lays down a comprehensive set of guidelines in its handbook, and some of them are worth repeating here:

A Clerk of Works should be of known integrity, intelligent and vigilant in the performance of his duties, possessing not only the practical knowledge of the various building trades, but some experience in measuring and valuing both work executed and raw materials. He will need to combine a certain amount of official or clerical knowledge with that of a more practical nature. He should be properly and liberally remunerated, that he may be placed above the many temptations that beset his situation.

It is always good policy at the start of a contract for him to have a chat with the Contractor's site agent or manager, to try to understand their respective duties and the loyalties they each owe to their employer. They may have to work together for three or four years so it is important that an harmonious relationship be established from the beginning.

But no guide-dog ever had to cope with the range of duties expected from a Clerk of Works on a building project. I'll list a few:

1. Check drawings for obvious errors in dimensions and detail. Compare with bills of quantity and specification for discrepancies between those of Architect, Engineers, Contractors, and Sub-contractors. Report accordingly to Architect.

2. Check base lines, setting-out and site levels.

3. Check progress of work against contractor's schedule and report delays to Architect with reasons offered.

4. Check all positions, dimensions and plumb levels of all formwork before concrete is poured, including structural members, walling, etc.

5. Take samples of all concrete pourings, retaining test cubes suitably labelled for identification purposes.

6. Check structural steelwork; check reinforcement quality, sizes, cover, spacing and fixing against engineer's drawings. Check placing and fixing of conduit and pipework runs for compliance with structural and architectural requirements.

7. Check drainage and plumbing layouts, falls and jointing for workmanship, standard practice, and compliance with drawings.

8. Assist Q.S. with measurements if required, particularly of foundations and work to be covered up.

9. Maintain contact with local authorities and statutory undertakings.

10. Maintain a daily record of the following:
    a. Number of men of each trade on site.
    b. Weather conditions and temperatures.
    c. Visitors to site.
    d. Drawings received.
    e. Work on which each trade is engaged.
    f. Delays – with reasons.
    g. Deliveries to site and details of shortages.

    h. Verbal instructions from Architect, Consultants, etc.
11. Include all (10) in weekly report to Architect, together with comments on drawings or information required.
12. Be on site at all times unless job necessitates visits to workshops, local authority, or Architect's office. In any case supervise mixing and placing of all concrete.
13. Try to anticipate and foresee difficulties on site and advise Architect in good time so that necessary instructions can be issued.
14. Be careful about giving advice to Contractor and others on their methods of work (for which they alone are responsible) lest it be interpreted as instructions and give rise to extra costs or other difficulties.

With a trained 'guide-dog' of that calibre it's hard to understand why Clients or Architects ever worry about what's happening on site during their absence. But they still do!

Index